Artemis Blu
AND THE
Solarium
Multiversity

Shanna Dobson

Unicorn Solarium Press

Artemis Blu and the Solarium Multiversity is a work of fiction. Some incidents, dialogue, and characters are products of the author's imagination and are not to be construed as real. Where real-life historical figures appear, the situations, incidents, and dialogue concerning those persons are based on or inspired by actual events. In all other respects, any resemblance to actual persons, living or dead, events, or locales is entirely coincidental.

Copyright © 2018 Shanna Dobson

More information at unicornsolariumpress@gmail.com

ISBN: 978-0-578-49202-5

Library of Congress Control Number: 2019904215

TO SWEET SASHA, LANLAN, &
JIMMY IMMORTAL LOVINGLY

CHAPTER 0

DIAPSALMATA OF LIGHT

HANNA ALWAYS THOUGHT TIME WAS A SOLARIUM.

CHAPTER 1

STAR DIALETHEISM

"IF WE UPGRADE WITTGENSTEIN, WE COULD POSSIBLY have a light language," Shanna daydreamed clutching her purple locket and twirling her red hair. Continuing the dream and continuing the day she thought to herself. "If we replace Wittgenstein's propositional logic with a paraconsistent F-theory variety, then poof we have a propositional analogue of light!"

The nurse begged again. "Will you please eat, my dear? The carrots are soggy with resignation and the applesauce is gummy." Shanna was eleven, transinfinitely so, since her eleven life units were counted in surreal numbers. She was never commensurable with all things finite and was a master at sustaining lucid dreams, since this was all one miracle frequency anyway.

"One day I will be able to eat light rays, organically grown light rays. But do light rays experience time? Would the light rays ever go soggy?" Shanna thought to herself. "The speed of light is so much faster than the speed of sound, and yet the brain makes it appear as if what we hear is what we see, as if they are simultaneous, when we actually see long before we hear. However could that alignment actually be and what would we hear given a variable speed of light? Whatever could align with variable light? Can we have any notion of simultaneity with variable light?" But Shanna could not hold together two such disparate worlds. She could perceive the nurse but at the cost of the dream, so of course she stayed with the dream. She imagined biscuit vineyards and raining apples and so in that sense, there was no rush to eat. She accessed the circulation systems of the roots and felt the rain drop apples reflect the sun rays in the tilt of the Earth.

"Your aunt left you a present. I will leave it here on your bed, Shanna. Please try to eat and rest. I know you'll be happy when you leave." The nurse placed a plush pink bunny wearing a tweed jacket on the bed next to Shanna, clasped her hands in prayer, and walked out of the white jeweled hospital room.

"Is she a Carmelite?"

"Is she a Unicorn?"

Shanna saw the nurse leave, but could not acknowledge its happening, transinfinite in her Diapsalmata of light. A series of sad events removed Shanna from her home in space, so she was looking for her home in time. She clutched the bunny. His name was Jimfinity. There was something muted iridescent about Jimfinity's jacket, as if it lived in the light between a double rainbow, as if it lived in pure geometry.

"Where is home in time Jimfinity? If home is yesterday, where is yesterday in space?" Yesterday was always Shanna's looking glass. "Where is yesterday in time? I don't even know when now is. So when is yesterday? And where in space is yesterday? And where in time is yesterday? Time is thus no diffeomorphism invariance."

4

Shanna knew that the concept of *now* was so tricky to define, given the intricacies of the reference frame system plus the complicated neurologics of sight. She wondered more deeply. "It seems that light has no space. Hmm. Suppose the speed of light, c, is not varying. Therefore, it is a constant, but a constant of what?" She clutched her purple locket and continued. "Russell says c is a constant ratio of manifestation of space and time; for every 186,000 miles of space that appears, one second of time appears! Must light itself be thrust into the binary of wave or particle? I think not Jimfinity, because the interval between emission and absorption for a photon moving at c has length zero!" She smiled at Jim. "Now Planck's constant is a quantum of action with erg*sec units ML^2/T. Could it be more fundamental than c? Maybe every photon of light is an identical unit of action? And that makes time a proposition!" Shanna clutched Jimfinity and sat up in the bed.

"But if c is a mere ratio, I wonder, is space the recursively enumerable ratio of manifestation of thought? Does this ever end?" She looked at Jimfinity and continued. "Probably not, since the Halting Problem is undecidable over Turing Machines. Haha!" Shanna laughed and jumped out of bed.

"But how does one make time a proposition, or is time such that it is axiomatic? "Shanna paused. "Of course, Jimfinity! That's it! Time is nothing if it is not axiomatic. That converse is tricky!" Shanna twirled with Jim. "'And let there be light' is a parallel to 'and let there be time.' But what is the topology of time?" She mumbled to herself. Shanna could always see the topology of time in the black hole and if geometry was dynamical, what prevented topology from being dynamical as well? She hoped to formulate the mathematical structure to realize such a claim. "It would be a bit frightening if sudden-genus-change was unleashed upon us! Dynamical topology is so fun Jimfinity and it helps me investigate higher dimensional beings. For instance, do you think 4D beings have black-hole hyper-volumes as eyes, where the eyes are their topology?" Jimfinity made no reply, for he was still a stuffed plush. Shanna continued. "Can you imagine, bunny, if there were no time? All of my words would stack upon themselves in a veritable mess. It really makes me wonder if time itself is just one stage in the universe's topological phase change, for I don't think time was always here. It's all thaumaturgical at best."

Shanna stopped twirling and daydreamed again. She imagined two electromagnetic spectrums intersecting repeatedly. How could we define time and causality based on two electromagnetic spectrums and what kind of clock belonged in such a world? She imagined the clock. It would have two faces and two pairs of intersecting hands. One face was etched in zeta functions. The other was etched in aleph numbers and the intersection of memory and singularities created time. "But what happens between the discrete ticks of the clock? What happens in the gap, dearest bunny? Or is that an equilibrium realm beyond happening?" Shanna ran her hands along the white cotton of her night gown, which was actually a white cotton hospital gown, and slowly climbed back into bed. Thinking of defining a time off of the electromagnetic spectrum, a dark energy time, required sitting and much more directed thought than the earlier twirling.

She noticed the applesauce and the biscuits and nibbled them. "I wonder how quantum creatures cook? It must be so difficult to phase change with those uncertainty principles, since cooking requires delicious operator commutativity." Only when she was at an impasse in the dream state, did she notice her current place, although *current* is a difficult word here since Shanna could access any time dimension approached from any causal or acausal direction; like a non-equilibrium closed-system retro causality. "Honestly, what if there were three dimensions of time along with our current three dimensions of space? What is the meaning of a spatialized time triple (t_1, t_2, t_3) analogous to our canonical (x, y, z)? See, Jimfinity, if I could master retrodiction and entropy reversal, maybe I could master bi-locating in a double awareness. Can you imagine being doubly aware? Or, more than doubly, multi-aware and conscious of multiple experiences at once? I've been practicing."

She quickly pulled out two sheets of paper. On one, she created a mathematics exam, and, on the other created a comparative literature exam. With one pencil in each hand, Shanna showed Jimfinity how she could take both exams at once. "I don't think having two brains is sufficient to sustain multi-awareness. We probably need multi-entropy." She paused and smiled. "Or we need mastery of creating time loops." Shanna daydreamed of creating a time loop of herself. "It's so free here!" She exclaimed. Shanna put away the exams and resumed her twirling and previous dream.

"Why stop at two spectrums? There must be a spectrum per every possible particle". She imagined receiving her Doctorate in Mathematics. "I propose that the GUT of language is possibly a higher dimensional version of Wittgenstein's work, reading propositional logic through Godel's Incompleteness Theorem and the F-theory Higgsing-geometry of varieties. If noncommutative algebras replace spacetime, what replaces propositional logic but a geometric paraconsistent logic employing infinity categories?"

Shanna always thought the brain was an event horizon, a Fargues-geometrization of a Cauchy Event Horizon in the form of an algebraic variety. Synesthetes were wizard adepts actualizing geometric fibers to find the *localization* of the happening of an event, and Shanna came in through the life portal with this skill. Her daydreams came in harp crescendos and left like mirrors. But how do mirrors leave in frequency space? Old thought was black hole implosive and self doubt was a point of infinite curvature, but new thought, new visionary thought, which Shanna lived and dreamed for, was pure white hole explosion. One gauge symmetry of a delta function and complex life was made!

"But what if you could gauge it all away? Time and language are gauge symmetries. Of, though of what, I do not know." The clock struck 11:01 and it was indecipherable whether it was a.m. or p.m. Shanna was always upset at this *either or* and preferred time to be a *both and*. Why, in her world, it was 11:01 a.m. AND p.m., for her world had three suns and all exchanges were made in light years.

"Why are hospitals like hermitages?"

The doctor came in, but he had never really left from his last visit. She saw him as rather a *To-Doctor* than a *The doctor*, for something about his lingering presence needed an infinitive.

"   ," he said, but Shanna was not quite sure, as she knew she didn't hear sound. She was hearing her brain interpret the waves.

"One need only consider with more or less moderation how you don't hear sound," she surmised to the *To-Doctor*.

"   ."

"Excuse me, but do you have the place?" Shanna always felt awkward asking anyone for THE time since there were always many times in no one's possession and people were actually asking about their cardinality in spacetime. Space seemed merely to retrodict time. Space was the retrodiction of time.

"Do you refuse my courtesy?" Her mind wandered again. Is any place ever one place? All seemed to be blessed with a certain multiplicity and the all is non-sophistical. She imagined an immersive theater in the forest playing *Circle Time and Topology Storms with Highly Non-Topological Weather*. What a curious title! Shanna was always proud of her morning dialetheisms.

Her daydream continued. "Let us commence our collaborative narrative on a topological weather-happening experienced in circle time! Here we go! My name is Artemis. Artemis the Cat. I would have remembered that I am a pink colored cat, but there was a topological rainbow storm that disrupted my memory bank and changed my color to robin's egg blue. Her memory bank is like a Cantor set, it self-deletes and reassembles, and then reassembles and self deletes set Cantor a like is bank memory Her. What did I do to encounter a topological rainbow storm? The storm beautifully gave colors genus,

8

with pinks always genus 8 (8 for vertical infinities), whites genus 1, blacks genus 5, greens genus 7, blues genus 0, yellows genus 4, and dark energies genus 11.

"It is a Monday in the year 2019, but I already fulfilled my dreams for 2085 and I am so happy about that! There is a cat Nobel Prize in Physics and I won it. What will I do in 2019 now that I have won the 2085 Nobel Cat Prize in Physics? I love questions.

"It is still Monday. I remember lapping coconut milk in Coleman's lap while she studied her physics, writing in my journal of past future recollections that had yet to be collected, let alone re-collected. When the topological rainbow storm came . . ."

CHAPTER 2

ARTEMIS IN PERFECTOID SOLARIUM

SHANNA AWOKE AS A CAT, WHICH WAS NOT OUT OF THE ordinary, as all felines were topologically bi-rational, and Jimfinity acquired a metabolism and could speak!

"Hi, Jimfinity! How do you like your pink fur? You're more alive now."

"Hi, Shanna! I love the pink with the tweed. I am far more alive now and you're now a white cat with OZ eyes." Shanna had daydreamed for years about becoming *Artemis the cat* and was calm about her new ever-transmogrification.

"Yes I noticed that myself. I shall call myself Artemis."

"A fine name!"

"Jim, I'm glad we have new forms. But have you noticed there is no spacetime here? As in, no space and no time? It is all very unlike octarine daydream time."

"I have noticed, Artems. Also how is there an *is* but there is no spacetime?" chuckled Jim.

"Maybe, since we don't hear sound we don't truly see time?" Jim paused and Artemis continued on. "Have you also noticed that we are not truly speaking? There is no sound here in this omni non-space, for there is no space and thus no longitudinal compression from which to make sound. Unless maybe there is a dark energy sound, but how does mirror matter ambulate?"

"Well, there is work being done on fifth dimensional dark energy as massive gravity and negative mass photons."

"Massive gravity is interesting. The energy neurologics of that are also interesting. If the brain is a Higgs field, then the act of thinking would break mass symmetry and realize communication across all scales due to the symmetry breaking. Perhaps neurons are just scalar bosons?"

"Perhaps. Scaling that idea, if neurons are tachyons, then the brain as a Higgs field could break negative mass symmetry and we could communicate without longitudinal compression!"

"Yes! Perhaps we are in a negative mass space? Thought breaking negative mass is truly baffling. Let us see if we can hear ourselves!" They both attempted to no avail and there was still no spacetime. Artemis recalled her newly furry body. "I wonder if the topology of fur has anything to do with the topology of time, because somehow I gained fur and lost time?"

"All distinct topologies are relatable in the Gap" replied a winged Fire Stallion with geometro-topological hair. Artemis peered around to see a glowing red stallion fluttering before her. Fire Stallion spoke in topological sound.

"Negative mass space uses topological sound."

"Topological sound sounds extraordinary! If I may ask, glorious Stallion, who are you and why does negative mass not permit longitudinal sound?"

"I am Fire Stallion and you are happily in the set-theoretic equivalent of a negative mass space; the aleph land, the crystalline quanta of time. And that is why."

"You mean, we are in the discretization of time?"

"Precisely. In the fundamental unit of time, the time crystal."

"But I thought time was endless."

"As endless as a lattice, and forever pixelated as a lattice."

"But how are negative mass and time crystals relatable and how does one sustain negative mass?" Artemis did not know of any relation between topology and mass, let alone negative mass. What was the relation between time and mass? Fire Stallion answered.

"Once you've figured that out, you can leave, but only then." She split herself into her many worlds copies. Artemis was so amazed! She knew that if she was quantum at the cellular level, then she should be able to scale the quantum properties and bi-locate or fission upon request.

"Incidentally, does this the aleph land have a Hilbert Space address?" Jimfinity exclaimed.

"Yes. $\aleph_0 \otimes \aleph_\infty \otimes$ Von Neuman Paradox."

"Wow. That address is a tensor product of uncountable infinities and the quantum observer problem!" Jimfinity exclaimed as Artemis deeply reflected.

"Even if I find the relation between negative mass and time, if everything is topologically similar, and everything is infinite, how can we ever leave, for we are below the level of entropy and cannot move a quanta of a time crystal? Is my transitivity here mistaken?" Fire Stallion collapsed her many world selves into one and approached Artems gently.

"Have you forgotten why you are so utterly preoccupied with Grand Unified Theories and upgrading Wittgenstein?" Aremtis paused and Fire Stallion continued.

"Have you forgotten why you are after the most grand GUTs? Why you can no longer sit with a rose but you must find its Grand Theoretic Equivalent?"

"Have you re-forgotten that I do both?" Artemis replied in pink clarity. Fire Stallion noticed Artems' adept tuning skills and smiled.

"Find the Grothendieck Solarium."

"Wondrous! Where is that?" Jim replied. Artemis was beyond familiar with Grothendieck's work and not at all surprised that he should be a destiny of sorts.

"You are in a pre-geometric affine space, my dears. There is no origin, so create a singularity and commence." Artems and Jim reflected, knowing the work ahead would be excitedly difficult. Fire Stallion turned to Artems and enchanted.

"Remember to keep your star." She flew off, never to be seen photonically again.

"Curious, I did not know I had one to keep. What lovely wonder then, that I have a star. I have a star now Jimfinity!" Artemis smiled and twirled.

"That's so exciting Arti! Let's use perfectoid entropy to create the singularity and ignite space-time, so we can find the solarium!" Jimfinity quickly exclaimed, keeping Artemis on track.

"Well, we are in a pre-geometric quantum space, so I'm not sure quantum entropy holds. Fire Stallion said were are to create a singularity and to use the relation between mass and time. Hmmm. I think a beautiful thought is a delta function, which is a singularity, and ADS/CFT duality is a field-theoretic relation between mass and time! So we can use the ADS/CFT duality, which maps higher gravity pre-geometry to lower non-gravity thought and leave negative mass!" With a non-local immediacy, Jim and Artemis appeared in an emerald forest.

"It worked!" said Artemis. "And longitudinal sound works again."

"And entropy!" Jimfinity brushed the grass stains off of his pink fur.

"Is there anything more beautiful and delta-function-making than an emerald forest?" Artemis chuckled. "Let's have a look!"

14

CHAPTER 3

NONCOMMUTATIVE FOREST IN INCOMPOSSIBILITY

THE FOREST CONSISTED OF TWO LARGE PATHS. THE path to the right was an emerald forest, which glistened in microtonal greens. The path to the left was also an emerald forest, but housed a sign at the entrance, which read *Our apologies. The Emerald Forest is Closed for renovations. Please take Alternate Path. Ordinance 7a*. Being a cat, of course Artemis immediately took to the construction path.

"What are those symbols? Let's go Jimfinity! Who has the power to close a forest and what possible renovations could be done?" Jimfinity looked curious at Artemis, as he saw no symbols on the sign, only words, but he supported her direction. They quickly jumped over the sign and were immediately aghast. As their eyes adjusted to the emerald, the emerald broke into thousands of impossible colors. These colors and the strange combinations of otherwise in-ordinal objects in the forest were so profound that it seemed as if there were two electromagnetic spectrums lying perpendicular to each other! They had never seen a vertical dimension to color. What did that even mean? The spectrums were not linear-horizontal, but were circular in shape, so they connected at their ends, forming a double infinity loop. Nothing *ended* in this forest. Red objects effortlessly turned violet and vice versa.

"Look, Jimfinity! The trees and flowers all connect! Where one branch *ends* a flower begins." Artemis suddenly noticed her upper body was split down the middle, with her left half completely invisible, her right half revealed all her bones, and right down the middle her fur was red orange yellow green blue indigo violet.

"Artemis! What's happened to you?" She shrieked and ran until her normal fur color and frequency spectrum returned. "I don't know, but that was incredible!!"

"Well, please do be careful!" They carried on through the flicker trees a bit further until they came upon a single looking-glass cloud, sparkling twenty shades of glitter white and suspended three feet from the ground.

"It seems rather odd for the cloud to be sitting so low. Well, we should say hello." Artemis thought.

"Good day, fellow Cloud!" Jimfinity began.

"Why, good day, dear Bunny the great," replied the Cloud by spewing x-ray lightning out of its top and gamma rays from its back. Everything in the path of the gamma rays was blasted away, only to be replaced by numbers, and then reverted back to its original object form.

"Wow! This is no ordinary photonic light." Artemis smiled.

"And this is no ordinary cumulus!" Jimfinity exclaimed.

"Do pardon our construction!" The cloud spewed. "This is normally one continuous beautiful emerald forest. However, we have been ordained to create a light language and a gravity language and, to that end, we must do surgery on the electromagnetic spectrum, sewing together it's ends in a feat of dimensional creating and gluing together its multiple gauged copies. Have you ever created a dimension?"

"Why, never!" Artems screamed, amazed. "Jimfinity, what on earth is a gravity language?"

"I can assure you there is no such thing on Earth!" Jimfinity chuckled.

"Have you ever created a light language? Or a CPT symmetry, which are the same up to isomorphism?" Artems shook her head in amazement. This cloud was an adept at advanced physics.

"You will in time, En time" replied the Cloud spewing radio waves from its top. These rays continued up forever. "Scale is breaking and we must defend our world from the destroyers of symmetry. Do you see how the scale here deceives?" This was mostly inaudible as the Cloud was in deep thought.

"Arti, look!" Jimfinity hopped to the closest object in view, *closest* being a curious misnomer since the distance from A to Z in this forest was the same as that of A to B. Artemis too noticed this strange *all at once-ness* of the forest.

"The forest is asking, 'Why believe in the pre-set scale?' Why, Jimfinity, I bet we could walk right through this forest, if we did not believe it was there." Why was the forest so keen on breaking the old pattern of perception and who were the destroyers of symmetry?

"Would you please reverse the way you came and continue on the other path? I have orchestration here to finish," ordered the Cloud.

"Yes, we are so sorry for bothering you! Just one more question, if I may ask. What are those symbols on the sign?"

The Cloud stopped spewing and the whole forest became the brightest white, as if it had supernovaed out of its color.

"My goodness. You have seen the symbols no *one* can see. I should not have given you that memory."

All of a sudden, Artemis and Jimfinity found themselves at the original fork. The path of construction was gone. They studied each other curiously.

"My goodness, Jim. This is turning out to be quite the adventure."

"Whatever did he mean by *giving you that memory*? You see, Arti, I did not see the symbols you did. I wonder what is in your eyes that made you see what I could not?"

"I've no idea, my friend. Let's continue on, before it is too late. To the Grothendieck Solarium!"

They entered the Emerald Forest, a sacred order of clock trees. The trees were in continual bloom and, yes, they were blooming clocks! Clocks of all colors, and sizes. No clock ever fell to the ground. Upon further inspection, the clocks were shaped like spheres with two pairs of orthogonal hands and 8×10^{53} clock numbers arranged in the curious pattern $\{-\frac{1}{2}, -\frac{1}{12}, -1.4603545, 2p^{1/2}, 2.712, 1.645, 1.202, 1.0823, \ldots\}$. Artemis read the pattern out loud to Jimfinity.

"$\{-\frac{1}{2}, -\frac{1}{12}, -1.4603545, 2p^{1/2}, 2.712, 1.645, 1.202, 1.0823, \ldots\}$"

"What is this curious pattern?

"$-\frac{1}{2}, -\frac{1}{12}, -1.4603545, \ldots$ It so seems familiar . . . Wait is that a . . . ?" But before she could complete her thought, she was interrupted by a terrible non-chromatic sound coming from deep in the forest. "What was that?" She looked around to Jimfinity.

"Sounded like it was coming from over there!" Artemis looked back at the clock and the entire array of clock trees had vanished, replaced with Nobel Pinkwoods.

"Either everything lasts or nothing lasts in this forest."

"I am just as perplexed as you, my dear. But, come, Artems! Lettuce go see what the frenzy is about!"

CHAPTER 4

THE MULTIVERSITY IN SOLARIUM

AKING THEIR WAY TO THE MIDDLE OF THE wood, Artems and Jimfinity saw a multitude of chalkboards flying in the sky, each covered in thousands of equations, and each scaled to the size of the CERN.

"What in the . . . ?"

"How exciting, Jimfinity! It must be a mathemagician duel." They had stumbled upon the prestigious infinite prestidigitorium of mathematics, the Multiversity.

Exquisitely, the Multiversity was made of Feynman Diagrams, with nodes of hypergolic self-assembling schools of thought. It was incredible! The Philosophy School was intersecting with the Futurist School and emitted the Physics School. This continued ad infinium in proportion as the schools of thought self-assembled. The schools of thought were just as aware as the creatures inhabiting them. This was the model of life as Artems had imagined: thought as delta functions combining in hyper-geometric Ramanujan series to produce complexity, which was life.

"Look Jimfinity! It's the delta function model of life I earlier imagined! Can you keep up with the interactions? It's all happening so fast!"

"Incredibly so. Look Artems! The Pink Glass!" Artems gasped. "I do believe we've found the miracle frequency."

Suspended eleven feet above their heads was the Pink Glass, a strange topological equivalent of a pure, self-sustaining life force. The Pink Glass was a Majorana particle with indefinite shape. It housed multi-species children who looking-glassed superparticle star systems in their minds. The children were also Majorana particles, so they communicated purely on the inner star charts in Grand Unification.

Peering through the bottom of the Pink Glass, Artemis saw children looking at other children, with monastic, clear faces, beaming multicolored gravitino star charts out of their eyes and projecting them onto the glass, where they bounced in star radiative transfer. Other children beamed OZ green Kac Moody algebras and sapphire S-duality Modularity proofs out of their minds, projecting them onto the glass, where they bounced per the illumination problem. Child Pleaidians beamed golden muons from their minds, projecting them on the wall and calculating Mirzakhani's geometric ergodic transfer. Child centaurs projected from their minds the neutralino timelines of every Multiverse species at every time epoch, beamed them onto the glass, and read the timelines through negative energy densities and coupling constants. They knew no mediation and they did not wait. They were in solarium.

They did not wait for the longitudinal waves to verbally speak nor for the photonic light to build a single world line. They were masters of entropy manipulation and number-theoretic manipulation of all twenty fundamental constants; they fully experienced whatever was beamed. The Majorana adepts smiled in Grand Unification with clear minds and laughter would change the color of the beams to bright pink, while adept concentration turned the beams blue, and clarity and local divination turned the beams OZ. The creatures in the Pink Glass never aged and never left the Pink Glass.

Artems and Jimfinity were utterly enchanted. Only an interaction with something as magical as a Multicorn could break their enchantment. A winged Multicorn in a houndstooth jacket quickly approached them.

"Welcome, welcome, welcome to the Multiversity, precious Artemis!"

"Why thank you blessed Multicorn! I cannot believe the Multiversity is an alive Feynman Diagram!" Artems was still in shock from the Pink Glass, which ascended high into the sky.

"My pleasure. Isn't it wonderful?" The Multicorn motioned to the trailing Pink Glass and smiled knowingly. "Ah yes, the Majoranas. They are their own mirrors. They are our mathemagicians." Artems and Jimfinity smiled their enchantment. Of course, future mathemagicians lived in the sky. Multicorn continued. "They need new symmetries to solve the time-equivalent of massive gravity breaking diffeomorphism invariance. For every L-function there is a Reimann Hypothesis. And, for the Majoranas, time is an illumination problem."

A strange shade of white passed through Artems' leg.

"How in the . . . ?"

"That is Tractatus! She is the gravity wave cat, visible only as contrast shades of mass." The shade of white passed through her other leg. "Do not be afraid, your DNA is safe from her $10^{-21}m$ happenings." Jimfinity giggled and Artemis jumped with joy. "Here he comes! This is Fiber Bundle, the Multiversity dog. Of course he is his own, but he lives here with all of us."

"But, I only see a collection of points," Jimfinity replied.

"But, those points assemble into a dog in the higher bundle space. Those spots are the images of his actual fiber foliation." Artemis and Jimfinity happily greeted the collection of points. "Have a look around and do not beware the looking-glass adepts. They may body swap with you to practice their RA lessons on density reassembly, but they are truly harmless!"

"Adepts?" Artemis asked.

"Yes, adepts of all species. They are our top neuro-cryptographers, along with the gravitino planets freely altering their Higgs field." Artemis glowed.

"Planets live here too?"

"Yes, although they don't have enough subjectivity to fully incarnate. It is quite fun to watch them interact with the Higgsino-Neutralino stars." Artems imagined a supersymmetric star.

"I bet! But, is it safe for us to tour the Multiversity if we are not yet an adept? The collisions look incomparably grand and the Higgsinos are supersymmetry stars!"

"A fine question, indeed. The Multiversity is built with massive gravity. With respect to the reference frame of the Schools themselves, there is no collision and you can walk right in and attend their lectures. The Schools are modeled across all time scales, merging into a negative-dialectic-Harkness-Plato Shellyian Academy. It is only with respect to the outside reference frame that the Schools are a-Feynman-Diagraming." The Multicorn chuckled with glee and Artems and Jimfinity smiled in amazement. "I must be going now. Mind the scaled-phenomena as we are manipulating the fundamental constants. Have a look at our PHD programs and the electives of prestidigitation, and do come study with us some light year."

Artems found it peculiar he invoked a distance unit and not a time unit. Well, many things were wonderfully strange here, but this anachronism perplexed her.

"May I ask you one more question? Why do you use light years as the metric currency?"

"Actually, the G-torsor is our internal currency. The light year is our external currency."

"Wow. Well, is there any time here? May I ask what time it is?"

"Time?" Multicorn paused. "Was there ever a more mortal tautology?"

Artemis reflected.

"Time is a dialetheism codimension infinity and thought is codimension 0, all in solarium. Our world is held together by thought. It's structure is thought, endless thaumaturgical thought. Not time."

Artems was enchanted by a beautiful octarine bright light shining in the sky. Jimfinity could not see it.

"It's beautiful you have octarine stars here, Multicorn." The octarine light glistened across her purple locket. Multicorn smiled with glee.

"That, my dear, is the Multiverse Solarium. Located in the causal diamond, it houses our most astute Professors of Light, working on the Etale Cohomology of Diamonds in the Diapsalmata of Light. I am happy you can see it." Artems dreamed of one light year entering the Solarium.

"Are the profs made of actual light rays?" Jimfinity inquired.

"They are made of all possible tensor networks of the Higgs Branch, which we colloquially call light."

"So, they are pure mirror symmetry gauges?"

"Precisely. Our Professors of Light are adepts of all things thaumaturgical." Jimfinity stood amazed. Multicorn handed Artemis an assuming dynamical pamphlet listing the electives of prestidigitation: Muon Lessons, Finding your Level 1 Twin, The Gepner Point of the Multiverse Levels, Elliptic Curve Transportation, 4D time, Gravity Wave Sports, Multispecies Economics, Light Year Currency, Ra Density Shifting, Multiverse Neurology, Quantum Cooking, Quantum Neurology, The Cantor Set as Observer, Magnetohydronamics of Multi-Sun systems, Negative Dimensions, Negative Dimensional Moduli Space. The list kept growing. Electives were adding themselves with the approval from previous electives. Artemis cheered and could not believe the wonder before her. Her purple locket glowed. The Multiversity itself was a singularity. However did Artemis and Jimfinity stumble upon such a place?

"However do you all live here in such harmony with all of this dynamicism? You must have mastered sustaining resources?"

"Why re-source source? We just use pure source, for where does the mirror end?"

"I never thought of that." Artems paused.

"Well, there is enough Hilbert Space for everyone! "Multicorn smiled. "Do stay for the First Keynote addressing *Experimentation is Animagus to Totalization* and for the second First Keynote addressing *Becoming a Multiverse Being*. They should be wonderful!"

"May we walk around and listen to some of the other lectures as well? We will be careful to not disturb any of the creatures here, even the gravity wave cats!" Artemis laughed.

"Yes of course and do not worry! You cannot disturb them. They are multi-aware. They are not identified with seeing." Multicorn smiled and flew off in ascension with the flying chalkboards. Artemis shined in glee, thinking of meeting the adepts of multi-awareness. Artems always thought sight was a ratio of space to memory. She paused to reflect.

"Is a looking glass a solarium? Or is this a looking-glass solarium? And if so, with what are the Majoranas identified?"

"Lettuce wonder and find out! Where should we go first?" Jim-finity asked. Artemis chose the Future Physics School, as it was the first to pop into her view. They walked into the lecture hall and listened to two Pleaidians in red robes debating in vampire collect.

"I tell you it's a gauge artifact, the whole thing!"

"No. The noncommutativity of spacetime IS magic, but it is not the sorcery of which you speak."

"You will see in due time that space itself is a time-crystal."

"No! How could that be if there are no global symmetries in quantum?"

"Just like there is no true periodicity either! Imagine rotation without periodicity?"

"The nerve!"

"Listen. We need a CPT symmetric model to explain the CPT violation in our vacuum solution. So we can simply borrow mirror particles just as we repeatedly borrow negative entropy."

"All we must do is supersymmetrize the seesaw ratio of the neutrinos to get a new seesaw between neutralinos and gravitinos."

"The moduli space housing neutralinos and gravitinos is of codimension infinity. You might as well find a seesaw mechanism for universe-anti-universe pairs and all multi-collective excitations. Feynman diagrams for superparticle interactions are codimension infinity."

Jim and Artemis smiled at all of the amazing ideas, closed the door, and opened a second door where a Hilbert Space Pegasus and unicorn were debating the pronunciation of the superparticles in supersymmetry.

"You're definitely a strange quark!"

"I'm actually a charming quark! You're a squark!"

"Yes, I am!"

"Well, I'm a Higgsino!"

"Of course you are, Unicorn! Unicorniggsino!"

"The superparticle of muon is smuon."

"Smu-plus"

"Smuon-plus"

"Plus is only for tauon!"

"Stauon is pronounced S-tau-Plus!"

"Why not say them all at once! Stauon-plus!"

"Let's scale Supersymmetry to all creatures. Who is your superparticle, Hilbert Space Pegasus?"

"La soleil."

"I suppose the sun is supersymmetric to all of us!"

"Now that I think of it, are there any vanilla quarks?"

"Yes, but they are off with the graviton in spin-2 space"

Artemis giggled at hearing their debate and walked further down the hall to the Future Cosmologists.

"The universe borrowed negative entropy?"

"Oh, for heaven's sake! I told you it was simulated."

"Just because the multiverse is self-correcting does not mean it is simulated. Your logic is flawed!"

"Flawed?! My logic is paraconsistent, I'll have you!"

"A self-corrective multiverse is a contraction that containedly obtains."

"You are correct. Go on then. What else drove the Big Bang?"

"I already told you a higher dimensional star died and passed through our 3D world. So the Big Bang is a cross section of something 8D perhaps ?"

"Why eight?"

"Because of E8 of course! E8 is the smallest even unitary lattice. And the E8 is a cross section of something higher and is the symmetry group of the 248 Lie symmetries."

"Sure, but it remains to find the object whose symmetries are {Level 1, Level 2, Level 3, Level 4}."

"Could we not tensor this set to the Lubin Tower? So that, perhaps, the multiverse is a Scholze-diamond of a perfectoid space?"

"Oh, that is the zenith of mathematics! I want to talk about the cosmos of memory."

"I propose that memories are fundamentally tachyons."

"Grand! We can scale that and supersymmetrize it."

"Scale it yes!"

"Okay. Memory entails dimensional complexity and the moduli space of memory is a G-torsor in SUSY."

"Wait. I re-propose that memories are stachyons."

"What is the moduli space of stachyons?

"Has anyone shown that there exists a quanta of memory?"

"Well, there is research on how memories are quantum symmetries."

"I say memories are big data compression-scheming Twistor Theories."

"I say memory is massive gravity!"

"What is the dimensional requisite for memory?"

"One dimension of space and eight time dimensions."

"How about eight time dimensions and four space dimensions?"

"It's all emergent anyway, we might as well."

"What would it mean to exist in multi-time dimensions? Not in the quantum *many world* sense, but strongly classically?"

"We can start with adding an imaginary time axis. I'll meet you at the intersection of 2:00 pm and 2:00 Imaginary. So this is 2D time."

"What would 4D time look like?

"We can spatialize it. 4D time is bounded by eight 3D times."

"What does stability mean in 4D time? Is stability such that it only exists in the *3-space and 1-time* combo?"

"I feel we as life forms are tensored with extra time dimensions."

"Can we formulate big bang in terms of neural networks with nodes as delta functions and synapses changing from inhibitory to gravitatory?"

Next to the physicists were the Future Clockmakers I. Artemis and Jimfinity listened to two looking-glass wolves debating.

"You cannot model a codimension infinity as continuous."

"I agree, but how is time not continuous?"

"I'm telling you, time is discrete!"

"There is a fundamental unit of time?"

"Yes, but it is emergent."

"Hmmm."

"I wish to try different particle times. Why is everything STILL photonic?"

"Joyous!"

"What of Neutrino time?"

"Yes!"

"Non-observable right-handed-neutrino time."

"Whee!"

"Light observable left-handed neutrino time."

"Splendid!"

"Superparticle time!"

"Oh, dear me!

"Neutralino time!"

"Keep going!"

"E8 time!"

"Wheee!"

"There is black hole time and white hole time. But time according to whom?"

"Yes!"

"Haha! I mean where is time?"

The multiverse stopped.

The multiverse began again and the researchers continued.

"Yes! Where is time?"

"It is as if time is a time crystal and a WHERE?"

"Yes! Yes!"

"Where is time? Where does the mirror end?"

The multiverse stopped.

The multiverse again began again and the researchers continued.

"Even better! Can you retrodict a retrodict?"

The multiverse stopped.

The multiverse began again and the researchers continued.

"Is that a cardinality argument?"

"Do we need the axiom of choice to retrodict?"

"Let us explore non-photonic time."

"Gravitino time!"

"Great heavens!"

"Do any axioms hold in gravitino time?"

"Not hardly on the Coulomb branch."

"But what about Majorana particles?" Artemis exclaimed to the researchers, but they carried on, not at all noticing her.

"I want neutralino time."

"I want time to have a neutralino."

"Oh, this is so exciting!"

"Let us assume time is a SUSY."

"Splendid"

"If time is SUSY, we can parameterize it by a Shimura variety."

The multiverse stopped again. The multiverse began again and Artemis and Jimfinity continued into the next hall.

"Why can't they see us, Jim?"

"I haven't the faintest idea, Artems. They seem to only see themselves and Multicorn warned us of their density swapping."

Down the hall, Artems and Jimfinity wondered into the Future Masters of Divinity.

"Why would the infinite make us its incarnates, when it is already omniscient and it is the infinity category of itself?"

"What a fine interrogatory! I am not even sure the infinite is a *the*. It is what remains and is the mortal tautology of what has always has been."

They left the lecture hall and walked into the Future School of Design. Artemis passed a cantor set of dogs and measure zero cats debating the Dogmas and Catmas on current Grand Unified Theories.

"Okay everyone, listen up! We must upgrade the GUT models ASAP if we are to be considered the Galactic Representative of Transinfinite Design. We have, as of now, budding theories on the GUT of muon-based electricity, the GUT of quark-sight, the GUT of Level 4 mathematics, the GUT of mu boson-Time, and the GUT of language as a quantum language of all the timelines. Please attend the following Master of Divinity lectures on symmetry breaking, where we imagine the original ordinal, with all else a reflection, as one of the possible collapsed states of the string-theoretic 10^{500}. We need 10^{499} more."

Down the hall were the Future Chemists.

"What if there are no forces and no data compression schemes and there are only accelerated reference frames?"

"With respect to who?"

"Exactly!"

"Look, if you stayed accelerated, would you ever age?"

"What happens to cells at constant acceleration? I am speaking of a reference frame dependent metabolism."

"You really want to relativisticize ATP and DNA structures?"

"100 percent!"

"All right, let's do it! I always thought the double stranded DNA was a product of the entropic division of non-equilibrium thermodynamics. I've always wondered what is the dimensional prerequisite for having a twelve-stranded DNA?"

"I am not sure, but I do know atoms do not die. It is the binding energy which fails us."

"Let's make the energies torsors or twisters and we can thus immortalize."

"Great plan! First we figure out an ATP based on neutrinos."

They carried on to the Future Clockmakers II lecturing on the Scales of Time.

"Good afternoon, everyone. As you well know, we are after a Quantum Time." Writing on the chalkboard, a blue whale continued. "Look, fix a causal diamond. Then time is the eigenvalue of WHAT?" The audience murmured a bit as the whale continued. "I say time is either a negative dimensional moduli space, a local codimension 2 singularity enhancement, or a foliation."

A blue shark interjected. "You wish to geometrize time, to model it as discontinuous? I agree the gap in time is befounding, but answer me this. Time is the symmetries of what object? If, as Noether says, associated to every continuous symmetry is a conservation law, then what am I saying if I ask to what is associated a discontinuous symmetry?" The audience was silent as this was new brilliant thought.

Whale replied joyfully. "Splendid! If non one word commutative algebras replace space time, then what is the categorical equivalent?

We could go at this set-theoretically. What if time were an inaccessible cardinal?"

Shark engaged. "So that the gap is the continuum hypothesis or the gap is a nonmeasurable set?"

"Yes, but I still don't understand why time cannot be commutative?"

Artemis closed the door. "My goodness, Jimfinity! I cannot wait until I am at that level of category theory. I am barely at Yoneda's lemma and am trying to understand Riemann Roch categorically."

They wandered to the School of Future Poets where outside the lecture hall a love boat had crashed upon the imaginary. Inside, the poets were debating love in the dialectic of vanity.

"Is there a negative dialectic of vanity?"

"Adorno would be proud of us."

"If we can formulate it, yes."

"Well, let's try. Is vanity closed in the group-sense? For if it is, then nothing more can become of it in the dialectic. Only more false sorities."

"I say we blend negative dialectics with dialetheism and sustain what obtains."

"Okay, and let's ask what is the measure of vanity in this regard?"

"Sure! Let's complexify fuzzy logic and assign imaginary measure to truth values."

In the corridor, Artems and Jimfinity encountered the Topological Weather People.

"I say, are pianos genus 1?"

"That's a great interrogatory!"

Artems wondered what genus had to do with weather. The weather people heard her thoughts and replied.

"Be careful as it is raining pianos and all things genus 1 up to homeomorphism!" Artems looked at the sky and sure enough all things genus 1 were raining.

"We need higher dimensional rain."

"Yes! I hope it one day rains Fargues-Fontaine curves!"

"If someone would break the equivalence principle, we might have peace around here!"

Artems and Jimfinity dodged the genus 1 rain and ran to the School of Cosmology, where a Galactic Council of Fairies were imagineering.

"Imagine a graph with vertices delta functions. What if thought itself is truly a self-repeating false sorites, as Kierkegaard always remarked, and is therefore algebraic stacks of delta functions? I think we could make this a Lubin-Tate tower at infinite level."

"Can you gauge it away?"

"Great heavens. Gauge away the Lubin-Tate tower?"

"Yes."

"I'll try."

"But can you categorify awareness? I made some progress with my day-jumping assignment."

"Categorify the day and morphisms are ordinals. Make a 2-category a month and go to the next ordinal if you are dissatisfied with the day's beginnings."

On the opposite side (?) of the Topological Weather People were the Mirror People whose heads were mirrors. The Mirror People are to the simulacra what invocation is to devotion.

Jimfinity wondered. "Maybe they were working on formulating the mirror symmetric notion of love in the dialectic of vanity and they became the simulacra? They mirrored everything until they became actual mirrors!"

"That's profound, Jimfinity."

"Well, the Future Schools are clearly non-locally related. And perhaps the mirror people are a phase change in the state of simulacra. For, is the mind a mirror? An event horizon mirror?"

"I somewhat agree, but what kind of mirror is the mind? I've always wanted to be a looking-glass mirror myself. Not a mirror that simply reflects what is, but a mirror that reflects what can be."

"Well, the Mirror People would say to looking-glass everything until you become the looking glass itself."

"So the mind itself is a looking-glass mirror." Artems smiled.

On the opposite side (?) of the Mirror People were the Color People, tuning an infinitely stringed harp. Their DNA was made of color blocks. Color itself held them together.

"Have they no constituent particles?" Artemis inquired.

"It seems they are too fast for particles and maintain their group symmetries only."

"Is that an infinite harp?"

All of a sudden all of the Color People turned and looked at Jimfinity and Artems. Jimfinity smiled, but was perplexed.

"Why, Jim! They see us! How can they see us if they are not identified with seeing?" The Color People continued to look at them. There was something muted iridescent in their gaze, as if it lived in the light between a double rainbow, as if it lived in pure geometry. If their geometric gaze lived in between the double rainbow, where did they as color live?

"Perhaps we bothered their tuning, Artemis. Let's keep moving."

"Wait. Do you hear that sound?" Artemis interrupted. "It sounds imaginary. Like the tones are made of imaginary numbers."

The Color People smiled at Jim and Artems and then looked away and continued their tuning. Artems and Jimfinity were having such fun!

"Do you know what is most beautiful about this place, Jim? There is no lack here. Everyone is clear and creating for a present betterment! They are all portals in flight." Jimfinity glowed.

They walked into the hall of the Future Philosophy School, where a panel of eleven sky unicorns were discussing Deleuzian thought to an uncountable human audience.

Sky Unicorn 11 proceeded. "If you would please, if you had the time to please, if you had the time to, please elaborate on Deleuzian schizoanalysis read through multiplicity."

"There never was a more mortal tautology," chuckled Sky Unicorn 11.

"Your very existence is a tautology."

"Prove it, Sky Unicorn 7, for you cannot have occasion without giving."

"Find your nearest tensor network, remove a tensor, and a white hole remains. That is existence and, yes, that is tautological. For what remains cannot sustain while it obtains."

"Enough of this prestidigitonium, Sky Unicorn Persiflage the Great."

"Prestidigitonium is the solarium of GUTs" thought Artemis.

Sky Unicorn 11 continued. "We are all after a GUT of language. I propose we need a quantum logic to build the Adinkra language, which is a global reference frame language akin to local tensor network languages. It's basically scaling the tensor laws. My mathematical colleagues think we can merely attach tensor groups to species and decode their languages." The panel was in harmony about these ideas.

Sky Unicorn 7 applauded the idea. "The idea is indeed grand. So let us build the mathematical structure to hold it and avoid solipsism. What does S-Duality look like as a solipsism?"

Sky Unicorn 8 added. "What about using the structures of Lie algebras? Can we read continental thought through S and T Dualities and Lie Algebras?" The audience stirred and the Sky Unicorn panel smiled in excitement.

Sky Unicorn 11 continued. "Most excellent. I say we read continental thought through Adinkras and gauge theory, Fargues geometrizations, p-adic Twistor Theory, and p-adic Shtukas."

Sky Unicorn 7 chuckled. "What about reformulating Deleuze himself AS a Shtuka?"

"Brilliant!" The entire panel smiled.

Outside the Hall was the Grothendieck Cafe.

"I would love a refreshment after all of these glorious lectures!" Artems cried. "I wonder what future food is like?"

They walked inside and a sun-star spoke. "Welcome to the Grothendieck Cafe. What can you get you?"

"Pardon?" Artemis recalled the name Grothendieck from Fire Stallion and smiled because she was somehow not affected by her proximity to this sun-star.

"Please have a look at our menu."

Artemis saw two options: a white hole with a side of Pleiadian soup or spontaneously luminous perfectoid soup with graviton plasma flat bread.

"I'll have the white hole option please."

"That will be eight light years please."

It was clearly appropriate that the sun-star would adopt a light year currency and so Artemis paid with non-local light years, for she had arrived at the place where she did not need to know with spacetime.

"How do you keep the white holes in storage?"

"With homological mirror symmetry of course! We use dualities to bring foods here and we never need to cook, for we haven't that stable of entropy, you know. Now, make sure you consume it warm during inter dimensional teleportation."

"Oh, I'm just visiting the Multiversity."

"Well, it must be your special day because these options are only available for manifestation on the eleventh day of the white hole week. Brace yourself!" Artemis clutched Jimfinity and her purple locket. The exterior of the cafe glassed out.

"It's a solarium!" Artemis exclaimed. "However did that happen?"

"Well, I am a sun and Cafe thinks it is a Hot Jupiter and wishes to rain glass particulate. It's just a phase."

"It's my special day and I've found the Grothendieck Solarium." Artemis mumbled to herself, still unsure of the importance of it.

"But time is also a solarium and what does Grothendieck have to do with time?"

The sun-star brought out analytic equations representing the white hole. The equations were made of light.

"So that is how they eat here!" Artemis thought silently. She nibbled the equations. "Wow, these are delicious! This is sustainable and no creatures were harmed for us to eat!" Artemis usually disliked eating for she felt plants and fruits were equally as sentient, given their complex genomes. But she continued eating the light equations in hyper-photosynthesis as the sun-star agreed.

"It makes for a cleaner entropy too."

"Do you ever vary the equations used? I know geometric and topological equations represent white holes too."

"Yes we vary the equations daily for most, but we must always use neutrino equations for the Professors of Light."

Artemis and Jim left the Cafe and wandered into the Future Neurology School where a winged glass horse was lecturing to a multispecies crowd.

"Since we know there are no brains, we have made a bi-category and combined Donald Hoffman's Fitness Beats Truth Model and Coleman Dobson's *Consciousness is a Higgsing F Theory Gauge Symmetry*. We are working on making this an infinity category and a Lubin-Tate tower at infinite level." The level of sophistication here was astounding!

"Have you forfeited your work on thought being an event horizon?"

"No. Rather, we formulated it and scaled it's betterment. So just as we can remove the event horizon from the standard black hole model and get a fuzzball, we can remove the Cauchy horizon from the mind and get a fully actualized Level 1 creature in the small ergodic limit. Remember we seek a double awareness in our sun chariots." The crowd cheered and exclaimed.

"You may need negative dimensions and topological suspension for double awareness!"

"I thought memory was merely mathematical descent theory!"

"I thought memory was factorization homology!"

"What is the relation between computational complexity and the data compression scheme of Hoffman's $G(2,4)$ algebra? Is the $G(2,4)$ algebra an $E8$ error-correcting code?" The glass creature smiled and continued.

"Well, if he can map interactions into an orthogonal basis, he is discretizing the interactions. So perception is indeed a series of data compression schemes. The series must be bubble wrapped in error-correcting algebras, perhaps, to maintain the $G(2,4)$ $SU(2,2)$ isomorphism. It is a splendid idea! We need a Lie-Algebraic definition of computational complexity and we will need quantum groups for that or varieties and actual schemes."

"So different species have different data compression maps?"

"Yes. Space whales use $G(8,4)$. It's all a satisficing data compression mathematical scheme. Even time itself appears to be a mere acceptability threshold."

"I see the schemes of data compressions as neural networks. Recall Arraut's work where the synapse connecting the neurons changes from gravitatory to inhibitory during the evaporation process, considering black hole evaporation via networks. Does perception change the synapses from inhibitory to gravitatory?"

"This is most excellent." A blue redwood in the audience inquired.

"But what is the cohomology of consciousness?"

"A wonderful question, as always. Let me show you."

The glass creature drew the spectral sequences and Drinfeld towers, constructed the bi-category, and then hurled the chalkboard in the sky, ready to proceed with the lecture.

Artemis and Jim carried on to the Future Music School where musicians were building semitone systems based on Cantor Sets.

"Photonic sight itself is based on infinite semitones. The ratio is aleph:aleph. So what we see is what we hear. So with a Cantor Set semitone system, we could possibly see dialetheism and therefore see all many worlds!"

Compositions with irrational time signatures filled the hall, while scores of musicians played Calabi Yau instruments carved from Cantor sets. Artems had never imagined such a sound.

"Jimfinity these time signatures are so curious. $^{77}\sqrt{11}$, $1/\pi$, $8 \times 10^{53}/10^{500}$."

"Indeed! To what are they tuning?"

"Multi-star charts for mathematical stars!"

"Yes! They have mastered the relation between geometry and sound." Jimfinity's eyes glowed in supernova excitement!

Musicians were constructing the chromatic sound of mathematical shapes, extending the dimensionality of the Z/12 chromatic ring. Bears played light harps, zebras played gravity-wave percussion pieces, while a Hilbert Space snow dragon played an infinite piano, stretching all possible frequencies, whose tones reached all species. Two snow dragons were conversing.

"There must be a relation between the mass of the proton and the chromatic octaves in the harp?"

"I say, it's an equatorial relation."

"Sure, but let's scale it."

"No, let's shrink it. The twenty fundamental constants provide the geometry, which constructs the sound."

"I agree. I want it fretless."

"You want a fretless piano?"

"I want it all fretless!"

"Yes!"

"The semitone system is arbitrary. 12 bc of 3:2. So why don't we make it infinite?"

"I'm not sure we can hear an infinite subdivision."

"That would be playing in a space which is greater than rhythm and less than a note."

"Is it because of time we hear as we do?"

"Well, we are hearing time, yes? So, is it because of time that we hear time? I would say so!"

"Is time also a semitone system arbitrary in divisions?"

Down the hall from the musicians was the School of Future Synesthetes. Two snow-light leopards with eyes of negative index refraction were discussing microtonality.

"And what of the microtonal senses? There is a geometry to senses."

"I agree! Senses live at the threshold of color."

"Color crossed with DNA methylation."

"Color crossed with time in methylation."

"Time is DNA methylation."

"This is so fun! I can feel my DNA."

"I can too! What color is yours?"

"Microntonic golds, depending on the category number of the division."

"11:00 is always gold to me."

"11:01 is always pink to me."

"There is an infinite series from 11:00 to 11:01 and that series is where the color change takes place. It is in the mathematics, for mathematical existence is physical existence."

"I can feel time in my DNA!"

"I can feel the time in your DNA too. Sight automatically stimulates my density network. So time automatically stimulates my density network, since sight is time."

"Wow, that's a rare gift. Time is already mixed canonically with thought, so any permutation of that is nothing clever, time being blue and such. But your time is mixed with your density, so for any time interval you can access me using fourth density!"

"Yes! It is a rare gift. I have learned to honed it in, for it was once overwhelming."

"My time was mixed with mirrors for a while."

"Well, most skilled adepts see in mirrors. Congratulations on achieving that!"

"Thank you! It is difficult to sustain. But I will try it again."

"I think Majorana time is grandly mixed with all levels of the Multiverse. They are the true solarium synesthetes."

Next to the musicians were the adepts of Future Language, whose accents were galactic and measured in non-chromatic hertz. Artems had never heard a galactic accent.

"Can we do buffalo buffalo buffalo buffalo buffalo buffalo with mirror?"

Next to the linguists were the adepts of Future Engineering.

"But what happens to thermodynamics if the multiverse itself is Majorana? Can you still have a self-sustaining total order respecting entropy?"

"Of course you can! Can we finish our discussion on the speed of light."

"I know you want the speed of light to be not fixed."

"Yes I do."

"Can you imagine the conflagration implications?"

"Oh, live a little!"

"I thought you said time was entangled with light?"

"I did."

"Then if light is variable, time would be as well."

"Hello! That is the whole point! Time was not always here nor will it always be here."

"Okay. So, we need a new geometry for entanglement."

"Yes. I think light is entangled with time through Fargues Fontaine curves."

"Okay. What next?"

"We need to design ways to travel that jump multiverse levels. Maybe we can use microlocalization on Alcubiere drive?"

"Will that get us out of Level 1?"

"Or ergodic FFT."

"Will that get us out of Level 2?"

"Or flop transitions in illumination."

"Will that get us out of Level 3?"

"Or change your hodge numbers, if you think we are ready for the topology of time."

"Bingo! Let's tensor Alcubiere drive with mirror symmetry. The engine will be a series of these tensor products!"

"Grand! What type of material could withstand the local and global intersections of all four levels?"

"T Duality and S Duality."

"We could pad the vehicle with all possible GUTs!"

"Yes! We would need a GUT of transportation for that. And whatever is that?"

"Breaking the Energy Time Uncertainty Principle!" They gasp!

Down the corridor was the School of Future Physicians, where two glass doctors were discussing the current state of molecular reassembly.

"The world is non-local and electrons are sentient, since their constituent quarks obey ER = EPR. So, they can assemble without AI. AI is merely awakening and harnessing the binding probability energy between quarks and we can scale this to stringy-theoretico."

"Sure, but you will violate all conservation laws!"

"There are no global symmetries in quantum and so the conservation laws must be a local solution. We can break time translational invariance to break conservation of energy and therefore molecular assembly should be fine."

In the next wing, quantum surgeons were performing DNA transfusions on glass beings.

"Why is a glass being more totipotent?" Artems pondered. Heisenberg Doctors were performing probability surgery. "Nothing is to fear when you're dealing with infinite probabilities!" The Many worlds surgeons were literally sewing together a Nobel Fur's timelines.

"Okay, so you'd like to go back to 1661?"

"Yes I would."

The surgeons made a geometric scan of the memory bank of the Nobel Fur. The memories were Ramanujan series of tensor networks. The surgeons then constructed a series of mappings and excisions and redirected memory lines to 1661. They mapped the tensors to an array of light beams which they shined on the Noble Fur in a photosynthetic transfusion of time. And the Noble Fur vanished.

"We really need to upgrade this process and get the tensor network in frequency state for immediate bi-location. And don't say use astral travel. It's far too basic in predictive coding."

"We don't need the predictive coding model. If we had a fully actualized Level 1 being, we would not even need the spectral sequences of maps from tree to tensor to light etc. We actually need to go further and create ways to jump multiverse levels."

"Well, just as we can remove the event horizon from the standard black hole model and get a fuzzball, we can remove the Cauchy horizon from the mind and get a fully actualized Level 1 creature in the small ergodic limit."

"Splendid!" And the surgeons began calculating how to remove the Cauchy horizon from their minds.

All of the Multiversity inhabitants suddenly assembled in the main corridor for the Keynote Speaker Coleman Dobson, who was delivering two addresses at the same time, practicing her double awareness. Coleman was advancing to candidacy for her doctorate in mathematics. Multicorn introduced Coleman.

"Let us all welcome Coleman Coleshine Dobson with her double keynote presentation on multiple time dimensions and multiverse beings." The audience cheered and Coleshine began the double presentation.

"It's so nice to see everyone. Thank you all for coming! And a multispecies Veritas to all! I would like to discuss experimentation as a scale-invariant methodology and multiple time dimensions. I've always thought that to achieve a GUT of physics we would need a GUT of mathematics to discretize and therefore geometrize time, instead of modeling it as continuous. I've always wondered where is time and what would a world look like based on, say, neutralino time, for we all agree time is some sort of emergent tensor network, but emergent from where? Or is time such that it is neither a *where* nor emergent from a where?" The audience applauded and Coleshine continued.

"Can we imagine the geometry of time? This has magical set-theoretico ramifications on a multi-species scale, as a new theory of time could help our beautiful world become a multi-species interstellar civilization. We will jump through the thought looking glass and investigate the geometry of time and what breaks information symmetry to the profound *everything not forbidden is compulsory* axiom of quantum mechanics. When particles are mathematical possibilities and interactions are gauge-mediated SUSY breaking, should we not perceive in solarium multi rather than linear time?"

The audience cheered and Coleshine continued.

"In the follow-up workshop we will, using a dynamical blend of Harkness dialectic, put the lecture ideas to flight and learn the precise mathematical and physical structures requisite to geometrize time, and the implications of this vision-shift for humanity as a dynamical singularity. What does it truly mean to harness thought as an event horizon and how is this multi-species incarnate? We will discuss the major tenets of GUTs of mathematics and physics, how their super-structure holds the geometry of discrete time and holds thought as an uncountably dynamical event horizon, and summarily the implications for interstellar acceleration. Know your wishes, decipher these curves, and let us begin!"

Coleman beamed from her mind high into the sky a gravitino projection of uncountable elliptic curves. The Multiversity adepts knew to use the Ramanujan conjecture to decipher the curves. This was how they read. Within seconds, the adepts translated the curves and constellated the resulting statements. Each elliptic curve was a constellation and each constellation was translated into a group of sentences.

Experimentation is Animagus to Totalization

Q: What is the causative power of mathematics? The Mathematical 'IS' is axiomatic?

Quantum Complexity is Dual to Geometry. Thought itself is the ET Uncertainty Principle. How is there an existential quantifier but there is no time? Replace causal totalization with an animagus M-Theory. Develop Deleuzian analogue of Godel's inconsistency and dialetheism while recalling at ALL times we are behind someone else's event horizon. Susskind.

Q: *Spatial temporal relations are NOT predicates but dimensions?

To speak is to commit tautologies while sovereignty is nothing. Thought is a Hilbert Space of Possibilities. GUT model works in Higher Symmetry.

Q: What are the higher symmetries of time? To Exist in conformal infinity GUT of time.

Q: What Arises?

Thought is in now a Hilbert Space of Possibilities.
Language: Quantum Superposition -> Quantum Language of Paraconsistent Logic.

Diapsalmata *either or* replaced with paraconsistent *both and Light* light/timelike/spacelike language?

Philos: Godel Incompleteness with Decoherence.
Wittgenstein - Multiverse Game.
Read Wittgenstein/Godel/Derrida through Uncertainty Principles.

The New Brain and The New Dualities

To-Brain: What sort of brain could keep up with To-time? To-brain, -brain category.
How can we read the notion of "simultaneous" wrt To-time, 2-time, to-brain, -brain.
Is simultaneity background dependent? Simultaneous to what? If background is nonlocal.

MWT: Can consciousness branch per many worlds theory?
Geometry is dual to quantum complexity, entropy is dual to? Time is the duality of ?
Space-time replaced by noncommutative algebras, brain replaced by noncommutative algebras? Can you Gauge it ALL Away?
Complexity: Quantum complexity build the brain? Did time, Q complexity, or entropy build the brain? How much uncertainty can break the brain?

Initial Conditions: Brain is a reference frame so we geometrize a reference frame—can you fall outside a reference frame? Gauge away the initial conditions? What then is the gravitational bulk dual (of spacetime) of 2-time?

Summary: White Hole-ary
Math: Every "now" is Discrete Gauge Symmetries by Higgsing in 4D. F-Theory Compactifications Gauge Away Cosmological Singularities, so . . . ? What is the measure of thought? Noether mathematical symmetry. Poof!

The audience cheered and Coleshine began the double presentation.

"It's so nice to see everyone. Thank you all for coming! And a multispecies Veritas to all! I would like to discuss experimentation as a scale-invariant Methodology and multiple time dimensions.

"I've always thought that to achieve a GUT of physics we would need a GUT of mathematics to discretize and therefore geometrize time, instead of modeling it as continuous. I've always wondered where is time and what would a world look like based on, say, neutralino time, for we all agree time is some sort of emergent tensor network, but emergent from where? Or is time such that it is neither a *where* nor emergent from a where?" The audience applauded and Coleshine continued.

"Can we imagine the geometry of time? This has magical set-theoretico ramifications on a multi-species scale, as a new theory of time could help our beautiful world become a multi-species interstellar civilization. We will jump through the thought looking glass and investigate the geometry of time and what breaks information symmetry to the profound *everything not forbidden is compulsory* axiom of quantum mechanics. When particles are mathematical possibilities and interactions are gauge-mediated SUSY breaking, should we not perceive in solarium multi rather than linear time?" The audience cheered and Coleshine continued.

"In the follow-up workshop we will, using a dynamical blend of dialectic, recitation, and Harkness methods, put the lecture ideas to flight and learn the precise mathematical and physical structures requisite to geometrize time and the implications of this vision-shift for humanity as a dynamical singularity. What does it truly mean to harness thought as an event horizon and how it this multi-species incarnate? We will discuss the major tenets of GUTs of mathematics and physics, how their super-structure holds the geometry of discrete time and holds thought as an uncountably dynamical event horizon, and summarily the implications for interstellar acceleration. Know your wishes, decipher these curves, and let us begin!"

Coleman beamed from her mind high into the sky a gravitino projection of uncountable elliptic curves. The Multiversity adepts knew to use the Ramanujan conjecture to decipher the curves. This was how they read. Within seconds, the adepts translated the curves and constellated the resulting statements. Each elliptic curve was a constellation and each constellation was translated into a group of sentences.

Q: What arises?

Space and time are pre-geometric emergent mirror pairs, emerging from the symmetries of spin networks of quantum complexity. So humanity is the dynamical singularity between the black and white hole, constantly replacing old paradigms with emergent constructs, and thought itself is an event horizon. Event Horizon of What?

Time is a quantum symmetry and can be represented by a quantum group. Higher Dimensional Reference Frames: Singular Moduli Space as a reference Variety; Derived Category handles geometry of time. Imagine: Economics system based on time symmetry? Non measurable sets a result of quantum time?

Q: E11 realization of M-Theory.

SU(3) x SU(2) x U(1)
SU(3) x SU(2) x U(1) x ?
E11
E11 X ?
Mirror Symmetry: F Theory + Time = discrete global symmetries

Q: Time as Higgsing: Codimension 4 Singularities of fibration correspond to 7 branes -> SU(5) Gauge theory.

Q: Time is a Gauge Symmetry. DAG Resolution of Memory and All possibilities.

The audiences showered Coleman in applause and asked question after question. The Pleaidians spoke first.

"Are you tensoring E11 with time or with gravity as a group?"

"Well, if I can pass gravity through a Hodge filtration, then I can maybe do both. It's really just a DAG Resolution of Memory, making it a Mirror Symmetry in the Higgs Network." The philosophers inquired.

"You're saying spatiotemporal relations are not predicates, but are dimensions? Dimensions where?"

"In some sort of Higgsing multiplicity."

The surgeons wanted more information about the new brain.

"What sort of brain could handle multiple dimensions of time such as 2-time and, going further, time as an infinity category?"

"One without entropic horizons."

The surgeons nodded in approval and Multicorn concluded. "Let's thank Coleman again for her wonderful ideas!" The audience gave one more round of applause and Coleman smiled and everyone dispersed back to their schools to commence the new work.

The penultimate school Artemis and Jimfinity encountered was the School of Multispecies Economics in a Society of Light Years. Opening the door, they found the hall contained an entire ocean and a pink sun shining on two scholars who were sailing while debating the efficiency of photoacoustic tomography on ocean creatures. The conversation quickly turned to multispecies economics.

"We need a GUT of economics."

"What does that even look like?"

"Look, first we need to design a game-theoretico economics based on abundance, not scarcity."

"Clearly."

"We want abundance for ALL species so that the game theory equivalent of an index fund is palpable to a dolphin."

"Got it. Let's keep the G-torsor as the currency."

"Compliance. Scarcity in game theory is what?"

"An insufficient board or a board of integer dimensions. A true game of GO would need an infinite dimensional matrixand surreal numbers.

"Or at least a lower aleph or complex dimensions."

"If we merely look at the game of life, it is played on an unbounded board of gauge symmetries."

"Okay, back to the basics. I'm interested in redefining goods and upgrading the truth value of goods. So if goods are muons or super-particles or CPT symmetric, then do we need any other currency than light year?"

"You want to make distance a currency?"

"Sure, why not? Someone made time a currency. And distance is time in the right units."

"Okay. What about upgrading?"

"Well, I want to upgrade the truth value table of what is meant by *good*, for some goods don't have an absolute truth value. We need a 2D complex value system, including the perception of the buyer and seller. These two terms we must upgrade as well if we are using distance as a currency."

"Okay. How can we make exchanges in spacelike manifolds?"

"In daily retro causality, can we truly make any exchanges?"

"Right. Let's make a Grand Unified Theory of Language first so that we can communicate with the dolphins and see what they need. I can assure you they don't want index funds."

"Okay! Let's have a look." They jumped into the ocean and swam off to find the dolphins.

Unknowingly, Artemis and Jimfinity saved the best school for last, The Future School of Mathematics. They walked inside to a Diapsalmata of Light, a ceremonial gathering of wizards and advanced adepts, all multispecies.

"And now for her advancement to candidacy, Coleman Dobson will present her work on "P-adic Shtukas, Lubin-Tate Tower at infinite Level as a Perfectoid Space, and a derived categorial Hodge-Tate period map."

"I would like to first say that life itself is a spectral sequence with morphisms as delta functions in the Etale cohomology of diamonds." The statement was showered in applause.

"My friends, can we read mathematics through the intersection of infinite Lie Algebras and Continental Thought and therein explore the philosophy of a thought that includes higher mathematics? A hyper-Wittengsteinism? I propose that the GUT of language is possibly a higher dimensional version of Wittgenstein's work, reading propositional logic through Godel's Incompleteness Theorem and the F-theory Higgsing-geometry of varieties. If noncommutative algebras replace spacetime, what replaces propositional logic but a geometric paraconsistent logic employing infinity categories?"

Coleman was further showered in applause.

"I will now proceed and firstly discuss the future of constructing the moduli space whose geometric fibers are Drinfeld towers, p-adic Shtukas, and Fargues' Geometrization of the Langlands Correspondence." The audience awaited her thoughts.

"Scholze's work on p-adic geometry has combined two great visions: Drinfeld's realization that in the function field case, moduli spaces known as shtukas form the basis of the Langlands correspondence, and Grothendieck's vision of the theory of motives as a universal cohomology theory. He recently constructed a p-adic-Twistor theory analogue of the Fargues-Fontaine curve and Rapoport and Viehmann's construction and reformulation of towers of moduli spaces as local Shimura varieties, in hopes that the cohomology of the moduli space of Shimura varieties provides a realization of the local Langlands correspondences. We review p-adic shtukas and p-adic Twistor theory, the degeneration of Hodge-to-de Rham spectral sequence and the Lubin-Tate tower as a Perfectoid Space, and then consider a derived categorical analogue of the Hodge-Tate period map. For intersection cohomology, we defer to sheaves of E∞ where the multiplicative weight spectral sequence of a cohomological descent category is defined as the spectral sequence associated to the filtered E∞-algebra."

Coleman picked up a piece of chalk and the Hall disappeared. With a non-local immediacy, the entire Multiversity disappeared beyond any semiology. Artemis and Jimfinity stood in amazement and reflected.

"Jim, there were many things brilliant about the Multiversity, but the most brilliant was that all of the debating scholars seemed to be the same scholar merely refracted in time. This reminds me of John Wheeler's argument, but this one is an ontological *it from bit*."

CHAPTER 3

MAJORANA GLASS TIME

"As my great friend once said, 'Stand not amazed, Artems!' Lettuce not forget our journey! Which way and to where?"

"However does an entire Multiversity disappear?"

"I haven't the faintest idea, though I can hypothesize a quantum ontology."

"I say we go back to the Emerald Forest and ask the Cloud for guidance, his an energetic recompense. But it seems as if all cardinality is lost here and so I don't know where *back* is."

"I don't either. But lettuce try this way! I'm sure the Cloud will help us."

Artemis clutched her purple locket and Jimfinity felt her small refrain under all of her inner glow. He spoke gently with stellar clarity to reach her. "Remember, Fire Stallion said we are in the gap in between the smallest unit of time." Artems calmed at hearing Jim. "Why did you wish us here? Yesterday is your looking glass. You can see them whenever you want. They are always in your mind." Artemis breathed deeply. "Think of the Majoranas."

"Yes, you're right, Jim. They are masters of double awareness. I am practicing and I am hopeful but, must everything be a future memory?" A fractal tear glistened from her eye and grew larger and larger, uncountably so, in its splendid suspending.

"Holy goodness, Artems! That is a fractal tear!"

"Pardon?"

"Fractal tears are tears modulo infinity. Their presence indicates you are manipulating scale."

Artemis blinked and found herself and Jim nearly drowning, as the single tear now had so much volume that it had filled the entire no-longer-cardinal-defined space. They were confounded with the immediacy of the blink-induced scale change.

"But how did I . . . ?" Artemis cried.

"You've changed densities. Fifth densities easily change scale and access the dataset of everything they observe, storing sight brilliantly like a quantum computer." Artemis smiled.

"You took the Emerald Forest and the Multiversity into your mind, Artemis. That's why it disappeared. It's all in you!"

"What an impressive explanation divination, Jimfinity!"

"Thank you. I was trained to handle the highest thought. Now, swimming is another matter."

"It's true. The forest and Multiversity reflect my most inner thoughts. Look! The rainbows!"

Jimfinity saw one rainbow glistening over the water. "How many rainbows do you see, Artems?"

"Oh, so many! So many rainbows at once. Not multiple rainbows, but one rainbow that split into many. I just thought of a multi-rainbow and, poof, there it appeared!"

"This is a fine reminisce, Artems the Great, but can we get on with not drowning? Help us!"

"I'm too tired to think now, Jim!"

"Please dear! Try something else."

"I am all of the sudden so tired." Artemis slumped under the tear waves and Jimfinity caught her and they quickly resurfaced.

"Artems. Remember your star . . . Please . . . I know you can do it!"

Artemis had a thought and every Angel in every Majorana glass window imaginable awoke. Her weak eyes sparkled their radiant emerald as the thought came again. As the last of the towering tear waves almost sunk Artemis, suddenly, slicing through the tears came a purple reindeer on a grand sailboat. His name was Valentinas Floo.

"Take my hoof and get in!" Valentinas pleaded in a Capricornicus accent.

"The boat only has . . . but how can that be? It has only one side!" Artems faded in and out.

"GETTTT INNNN!" They each grabbed a hoof and Artems and Jimfinity pulled themselves onto the boat, greatly assisted by Valentinas, and utterly sacked and exhausted. Valentinas Floo was a youthful reindeer standing nine feet tall with purple sparkly fur and a tail which tuned to color according to his pitch. What made him absolutely extraordinary were his great eyes.

"Why thank you, Mr. Reindeer! Oh, my goodness! Your eyes!" Artemis smiled. Valentinas' eyes were composed of harp strings and each eye had a different number of strings. The left eye had only one string, while the right eye had eleven strings. The harp strings were colored alternately red and white and they connected the eyelids so that his irises were lines, peppermint lines. Upon blinking, the red color changed to white and the white changed to red, while the one changed to eleven and the eleven to one. This was dizzying to behold. Where were the pupils?

"What a curious tail you have! And eyes of harps!" Artemis joyously exclaimed.

"Why thank you! I've always said, why have a tail of ONE color, when I could have a tail of ALL colors?"

"So splendid! How does blinking cause the strings to switch sides?" Jimfinity inquired and Valentinas smiled as if Jimfinity's question was too small to ever reach the mechanics of the eyes.

"Time is a harp, dear Rabbit, where the strings represent years. To travel through time, all we need to do is jump string." Jimfinity listened on in amazement, utterly perplexed by the zodiac accent.

"I am not blinking as you think I am. I am traveling through time."

"While still maintaining a conversation with us?"

"Why of course." Valentinas spoke so casually, as he had mastered this time traveling eye technique long ago. Artemis and Jimfinity were not even sure anymore if Valentinas' eyes were indeed *eyes*. Artemis also noticed the numbers *111* engraved on his sparkly purple chest fur.

"What does the space in between the strings represent? Is that another form of time?" Artemis questioned.

"I do not know." Valentinas smiled and rightly knew the answer to her question.

"But I cannot tell if there is volume in your eyes?" Artemis mumbled inaudibly, but Valentinas heard her crystal clear and resumed.

"All we ever see is time. Hence the harp eyes." Jimfinity chuckled.

"How is your tail so easily changing color?" Jim wiggled his own tail and it stayed pink.

"My tail is more frequency than fur."

"I agree! May I ask one more question? I still don't understand how a boat with one side can float?" Jimfinity inquired.

"Dear Rabbit. May I first say what a nice sleek pink coat you have!" Jimfinity blushed and thanked him.

"Back to your question, where do you think the other side is? And is a *where* even the right question?" Before anyone could process this riddle, twenty Antlers fell from Valentinas' head and self-assembled into a red chaise lounge lined with six luscious carrots. Valentinas looked at Jimfinity.

"Were you hoping to sit somewhere?"

"Why, yes I was." Jimfinity blushed and Valentinas smiled. "Splendid! How did you know I wanted such a chaise and however did your antlers make it?" Valentinas' eyes blinked their red whites and white reds, which still had no pupils. So excited by his wish coming true, Jimfinity proceeded to sit and rest his hind legs, and scarfed down all six carrots.

"My goodness! All of this talk and thamaturgical mastery and we have yet to ask you your proper name. What is your name?" Artemis asked.

"I am Valentinas Floo, but I am not officially a wizard. Yet . . ."

Artemis enchanted on. "Did you study at the Multiversity? We just visited and it was the most magical place." Artems felt strange asking the question since there was locally nothing left of the Multiversity in their current version of time.

"I did and I was almost a Professor of Light." Valentinas paused. "But that is a bit of a story and since you two obviously have places to go and I must get back to work . . . do go on! I just don't think I have the time!" Valentinas galloped down the boat which seemed to have grown in length to ten times the size it was only minutes ago. It grew in proportion to Valentinas' gait.

"Jim, where would we go from here? We are on a sea of tears, having been rescued by a nine foot harp-eyed purple reindeer!" Jimfinity had a thought.

"Wait! We would love a good story and if you do not have the time, well I can provide you with a block of it." Jimfinity winked at Artems as a time block fell from Valentinas' antlers. Valentinas was in shock at this level of wizardry. He could time travel but he could not freely make time blocks. Valentinas turned around and leapt to Jimfinity in excitement.

"Brilliant!"

The time block was a thaumaturgical, topological mess. It disobeyed the asymmetry of time, by being equally capable of retrodiction as of prediction. It was as discrete as an inaccessible cardinal. Jimfinity held out to Valentinas a golden block with the number thirty on it, giving Valentinas thirty minutes to speak, all without violating conservation of energy, because it was, well, thaumaturgical.

"Proceed, Sir Valentinas Floo."

"That is extraordinary, Mr. Bunny".

"I am Jimfinity, the time loop bunny." They shook hoof and paw and Valentinas noticed his iridescent jacket, which lived in the light between double rainbows.

"What an exquisite jacket, Jim! May I ask what is a time loop bunny? Can you actually make closed causal curves?"

"Thank you! I am happy to explain. Yes, I can. I live in the space between recognition and interaction; the space of time machines."

"That is brilliant! A time machine is the space between recognition and interaction. And what are the energy conditions requisite to make a time loop? Better yet, what energy is required to sustain a time loop since doing so would clearly violate all weak energy conditions?"

"Wonderful questions! Are you familiar with Everett's Many Worlds theory?"

"Of course."

"Great! Well, I change the ambient space in which those infinite timelines live, and therefore I change the timelines. Timelines do not lie on a 2D Euclidean plane. They are analytic Cantor sets, which live in geometric moduli spaces obeying modularity conditions. I make the timeline *nodes* Majorana particles, and poof!"

"I wish I would have stayed and learned this at the Multiversity!"

"I think the Majoranas are new electives. It would be an amazing feat for you to learn!"

"Can we talk more of the timeline node? It is such a highly complex object, being a game-theoretic origin of uncertainty. If a timeline node is Majorana, it is mirror to what? And does this not give validity to all possible timelines, therefore rendering choice null?"

"Time is an illumination problem. So, there is still a weight function on the node. So, validity is not globally equal."

"I see."

"I could also make the time nodes gravitinos or tachyons. Can you imagine?"

"I can! I've often wanted to make contact with my offline timeline copies, but I worry about ramifications in the conservation laws.

"Those are valid concerns."

"Jim, if the time node was a gravitino or tachyon, I would be so happy!"

"I would, too! I think accessing those offline copies would greatly increase our currently low output-to-input ratio. We input so much and our output is barely one world. Truly that ratio governs the complexity of all forms, living and non."

Valentinas smiled. "I have a story for you both."

Artems and Jim poised, ready.

"I once saw a butterfly incredibly still. Everyone claimed the butterfly had passed away, but I had another thought; that she merely had one heart beat per year."

Artems and Jim smiled and Artems replied. "What a beautiful tale, Valentinas."

"Why, thank you, dear Artems. I never thought she had passed away. Merely, in her state she was less complex and lived below the canonical units of life."

"Complexity is related to timeline nodes as well, Valentinas." Jimfinity proclaimed. "Imagine the time-planes resulting from two dimensional time. Time-planes intersect in lines and what meaning have those lines? Imagine infinite sheets of time-planes intersecting. The intersection sight is now an object much more complicated than a multi-dimensional timeline node and it will beget new energy laws."

"Does it violate unitarity?"

"Not globally. We must read multi-time through the multiverse. Then we must read the time nodes as a spectral sequence and run induction on the spectral sequence."

"Brilliant! Are there any pathologies in the time-plane?"

"Sure."

"What would that look like? A pathology in the spectral sequence?"

"An illumination problem or a temporary bilocation. It has something to do with the output-to-input numerical invariant ratio."

"Can you explain this?"

"Sure. Again, I reference our complexity as our output-to-input ratio. We creatures input so much information constantly but our output is at most a Fields Medal and at least a smile. Imagine a world where the output-to-input ratio was one, for all creatures." Everyone was spellbound at this statement, mostly Jimfinity!

"So a temporary cut in the time-plane alters the output-to-input ratio. It may even apparate the ratio."

"It is as if you're using mathematical energy?"

"Is there any other?"

"You're right. I never thought to change the moduli space. So the time block apparates into however many units you choose? Like you chose thirty minutes for me?"

"Not quite. The moduli space which makes the time block is a mathematical power tower of all possible combinations of units." A small power tower fell from Valentinas' antlers, reading $a \uparrow \uparrow k$.

Jimfinity continued. "The block itself chooses the amount of time."

"The time block chooses itself?"

"Yes, like an energetic Axiom of Choice." Valentinas stood amazed.

"And what happens to space while the time block is ticking?"

"It is frozen in a microlocalized gravity."

"You're saying the time block is a time crystal?"

"Yes."

"So time is a mirror symmetry?"

"Yes." Valentinas stood amazed.

"But stand not amazed! You must hurry on with your story, as once the units are fixed, it is very difficult to add more time. I have yet to master those energy equations in that singular bundle space. The block will disappear once the time spell is over, broken by the higher space and space will phase change as is canonical."

"I see! I have only one further question. If there is a singularity in the timeline, what happens?"

"Aren't all timelines singularities?"

"Right. Let me rephrase. If there is a singularity in the fiber space which makes the timelines, what happens? What would it mean to have a gap in the timeline? And a gap in the timeline makes what kind of time block?"

"A gap in the timeline appartes into a time block of untime."

"So exciting! A gap in the time-plane is an output-input ratio and a gap in the timeline is a block of untime! Jimfinity, you have made my one-sided day!"

"You're welcome, Valentinas! Quick now!"

"I will be swift! I was born with the gift of molecular reassembly. I can alter the molecular gauge structure of anything lepton. My tail, for instance." Three more antlers fell off and formed a giant head of lettuce. Jimfinity smiled.

"My apologies! I was suddenly hungry with all of this time-plane talk!"

"Please enjoy!" Jimfinity listened intently as he munched on the crisp lettuce. Valentinas continued. "Anyway, my fawn friend told me I had the Phoenix power of alchemy. I could help anyone change any object at anytime, given their wish was sourced by pure intentions. I was also flying at an early age. My mother wished I joined the Hoofington Snowflake Academy school for precocious peculiar reindeer, but I thought I was more than a reindeer and that I could ascend to Wizard right away, all by myself." Valentinas paused." I did not need anyone's help."

Upon uttering this last sentence, Valentinas' eye strings completely disappeared from his eyes for a zeptosecond and then reappeared. Artemis noticed at once and wondered if it was a glitch. Valentinas carried on. "So I enrolled at the Multiversity and I had such fun! One day I was at work in the Future School of Physics trying to master alchemizing space and time to be able to stretch them at will. I was somewhat successful!" Jimfinity smiled in carrot-content. Valentinas smiled and continued. "As you can see, my antlers are magical future antlers. However, they continue growing ad infinitum."

"Look, Artems! Infinity Antlers!" Valentinas' golden antlers spiraled into beautiful L-functions and repeated forever up into the sky.

"Your infinity antlers make the most amazing enumerative geometry problem!" Artemis looked around from the one-sided sailboat and there was ocean in every direction. Ocean and antler-made wooden figurines. Valentinas had a gift, but he was stuck in a one-sided geometry and he grew more sad as he spoke.

"Well, while conjuring enough heat to make the future antlers, I melted my home, the Great Snow Land. I didn't even notice, as I was so involved with the antlers." Jim and Artems felt so sad for him. "It happened so fast. I lost everyone. My little snow-cat friend, Golden. I could not save him. All of the snow, gone and I the apostle of sorrow." The strings disappeared in his eyes once again leaving two white spaces where the eye harps would have been. Artemis wept, as she too had known impossibly fast loss. The strings re-appeared in his eyes and he continued. "The Multiversity taught me that I was entangled with my fondest thoughts and to be careful with them, that un-trained creation proceeded in proportion to fondness. And I . . . did not listen." Artemis whispered to Jimfinity, hoping Valentinas would not hear.

"Did you notice the strings sometimes disappear from his eyes?"

Jimfinity nodded and replied. "Emotion stops time and I believe that is his way of weeping." Artemis understood. "It is best we leave him alone and ask him of this no more." Valentinas heard it all but did not offer that he did and carried on.

"I was so sad that I lost my ability to fly. Everyone at the Multiversity was concerned. Oh, if only I had I first gone to Hoofington like my mother had proposed, then I could have been prepared, for reindeer cannot fly with doubt." Valentinas paused. "It's funny. My antlers can form everything imaginable. But they cannot make me fly. If only I knew that one small piece of the Snow Land remained. I never thought heat more powerful than snow."

"Heat may be more powerful than snow, but belief is more powerful than sadness Valentinas!" Jimfinity exclaimed. The time block read eleven.

"This is true. Anyway, I am not worthy of these powers. If only I would have noticed the snow melting." Valentinas carried on and on in this manner, his eye strings disappearing from time to time. Jimfinity noticed the golden block and knew he would have to act fast, for the golden block could only be summoned once. Jimfinity could make a time-loop back to when the mistake happened, so Valentinas could correct the error and regain his confidence and flight, when Artems scratched her head. Her eyes glowed emerald. A thought was coming.

"Worth . . . That's it!" She lit up with joy. "Valentinas, have you ever noticed the 111 on your chest?"

"The what?" Artemis could not believe what she heard. So she asked again.

"The 111? It is on your chest. Can you see it?" No one could see it. No one but Artemis.

"Hurry, Artemis. The Golden time is melting!" Artemis proceeded quickly.

"Well, those numbers are not just for any reindeer! They are the most magical numbers!" Her eyes glowed and the purple locket glowed. "The numbers are here to help you! You made a mistake! You could change the ocean back into the Snow Land and save all the creatures you lost!"

"But I feel so bad for the mistake I've made." Artemis pressed on with golden conviction.

"Forgive yourself and believe that the Snow Land needs you. You have the power to save everyone! Look they are all still there! Just in water form!"

"How did the melted Snow Land become Artemis' tear?" Jimfinity wondered to himself. Valentinas had never thought of the phase change! The Snow Land was still *there* just in a different form, as it had changed phase under his alchemy. Nothing truly was destroyed! And in that moment he realized his worth. He was given these powers in order to save his world. His eyes started blinking in rapid speed and he smiled eternal radiation. He began to lift off the ground. It was a shaky start!

"Be careful, Valentinas!" Artemis exclaimed. She noticed the 111 glowing incomparably.

"Wait? It can't be! I ruined everything!" And he fell back down to the sailboat, which was now no more than a foot wide. How everyone was still able to fit is another story.

"You can do it, Valentinas! You ARE worth it!" They smiled lovingly. Valentinas began to remember. He remembered his family. Little Golden. The Multiversity.

"You're right! Everyone is still here! Energy just changes form and all we see is time!" Valentinas was radiant again. The 111 glowed and he ascended with the confidence of a thousand Pegasus horses. His tail glowed all the colors at once as he soared gracefully and majestically into the sky. His eyes did their peppermint time signature.

"If I reverse the alchemy and use my future antlers, the Snow Land can return!" As Valentinas soared above the sky, he delivered an incantation that awoke the same Angels in the same Majorana glass. He changed the water into sparkling snow and the Snow Land was rebuilt, snowflake upon snowflake. He saw his family's home and all of his friends except little Golden. Artemis also saw a little snow cat who she thought would be most perfectly named Golden. But Valentinas did not comment. Maybe it was not Golden? He swooped down to Artems and Jimfinity.

"Let's away! We must find Golden!" Artems thought that if Golden was his fondest memory and if creation proceeded in proportion to fondness, then Golden was maybe somewhere far away. Artems and Jim quickly climbed onto his fluffy back and they all soared off. "My antlers have stopped spiraling! I can control them!" Valentinas had regained his sense of worth and his ability to control his powers. It was an amazing day for Artemis and Jimfinity. The great Snow Land was being rebuilt and the golden block of time read 0. Jimfinity smiled.

CHAPTER 6

SKY VERITAS IN MIRROR SYMMETRY

THEY CONTINUED HIGHER AND HIGHER UNTIL THE sky of white became patchier and patchier. Valentinas noticed color gaps in his purple fur, as did Artems in her white fur and in her purple locket, as if they were being color corrected in pixelation in real time. They studied each other intensely as they were blasted with the sounds of all impossible harmonics.

"Welcome to the Land of Mirror Symmetry," sparkled several female voices speaking like red-shifted sirens. The voices came from an ergodic portal beyond form, made of the event anti-horizons of every anti-black hole ever created. The Portal spoke a meta language composed of the voices of all Angels in Majorana glass. The Portal was non-localizable and she accessed a general memory bank. The Portal spoke.

"Everything not forbidden is compulsory." Everyone looked in every direction to localize the sound. No one was successful. "When you remember your star, everything not forbidden is compulsory." Artems recalled the words of Fire Stallion.

"Her form is impossible, so of course her coordinates are too! She's playing with spacetime symmetries." Jimfinity exclaimed.

"Are you sure it is impossible?" The Portal confided. It was as if dark matter mastered speech and everyone was absolutely uncertain about their whole quest. Who was Golden? All of a sudden, Artemis found herself split. Split in the mind, split in the body, according to all possible versions of herself and their Cantorian selves. Valentinas and Jimfinity experienced the same.

"Quick!" The many-Artems exclaimed. "Let's get out of here!" A door suddenly appeared. She reached for the door but her paw dissolved right through it, for it was no longer a door. She was experiencing everything all at once. The Portal spoke again.

"There are so many minds. You have to learn to have one. And then none."

All the creatures panicked in heteronomous unison. Artemis found herself struggling to hold onto any baseline reality, while being in this multi-awareness space of immediate manifestation. She molecularly rearranged into whatever she wished. She became all things winged and then all things aquatic, things including sentient creatures and things including dynamic geometries. Being formless would have been a profound experience, had she not forgotten who she was. She had so many nervous systems, which each had so many wings and so many aquatics, while she had no *one* to singularly act.

"Don't worry. The unicorns of unitarity will find you when you're ready." The Portal unremarkably remarked.

One half of Artemis' form returned in full white fur, while the other side flickered. Somewhat relieved, she looked at her friends and everyone was half-there as well. Artems repeated over and over again the Portal's phrase.

"Everything not forbidden is compulsory . . . . Everything not forbidden is compulsory . . ." Everyone was silent, still trying to decipher the meta code, when Artemis screamed. "Wait! That means there's a world where I've already found my future-memories!"

"Yesssss," cried a Great Codimension Infinity Phoenix swooping down from the uncountable harmonic beyond the heavens. In an instant, everyone's full-form returned. Kala Veritas the Great was a Codimension Infinity Phoenix made entirely of octarine glass with noncommutative wings made of thought-lattices spanning Lubin-Tate Towers. Inside her infinity shaped eyes were infinite sheets of two-dimensional imaginary time signatures. Her sight was made of imaginary compositions. Kala landed and bowed to Artemis. Artemis returned the bow in full-gaiety.

"You made it," said Kala. She sounded like the Portal. Perhaps they were the same creature? But what did it mean to be the same when one creature was made of event horizons and the other of octarine glass?

Artemis' friends all bowed in miracles.

"How do you manage such great wings?" Valentinas inquired.

"Gracious deer, they are not what you think or can you not see that they manage me?" Everyone studied her wings curiously only to see themselves and their thoughts in them, as if they were simply reflecting in mirror. But they were not and this was an anti-mirror. Jimfinity cried.

"It cannot be. Your wings are what we see!" Kala smiled and bowed once more.

"What is a vector bundle of beauty times a quantum flux of wisdom?"

"Magnificent! I know of no element that can hold that Aleph of infinities." Artemis exclaimed.

"It is no easy task, my dear Artemis. The Multiverse in its diffeo-morphism invariance is constantly weaving the fabric of existence through gauge symmetries and infinite transfinite infinites. But that is for your next adventure. That is not why you came here." The Portal spoke again from her impossible place.

"Mind your in is It. Here star cardinality no is There." Her words simultaneously broke apart and reassembled themselves in an endless repetition, terribly exciting and confusing everyone. Was Kala Artemis also? Valentinas exclaimed.

"Why is there no identity in this room?!"

"Identity is an illumination problem." Kala sounded. Jimfinity unscrambled the message.

"I have it! The Portal is saying, 'There is no cardinality here. It is in your star mind.'" Everyone looked at Jim completely perplexed. "Remember, Artems, cardinality is direction and Fire Stallion spoke of us finding the Grothendieck Cafe, which was a solarium at the Multiversity, which was devotion, which was time, which was Valentinas' heart, which was his wings. A Star Heart. Oh, Oh, Oh, but all of it in symmetry! It's all a Star Heart in Solarium." Putting it all together, Jimfinity exclaimed, "The world you seek is inside your Star Heart. They have never left you. Everything is here." Artemis cried and cried. "Just invent a new sensation by which you can SEE them. Somehow use the illumination problem and the power of the mirror symmetry."

All at once, everyone found their most inner thought space in their minds. They felt a pink orchid blooming in their heart and they realized the power of the pure thought space and heart space. That everything WAS possible when realized from that heart space. One by one they each wept with amazement and gratitude. Valentinas saw his Reindeer Academy and his beloved snow-cat-friend Golden.

"Golden !!!" He exclaimed with the tears of a thousand suns. Jimfinity saw his father alone weeping in his counting house.

"Father, I am so sorry. I did not know . . . I am right here!" Artemis saw her parents smiling and tending to their lilac garden.

"I don't understand . . ." Artemis wept.

"You can only see them because you are in the gap at once between time and beyond time." Kala gently refrained.

"But time is a solarium."

"Yes. Use its mirrors." Kala replied masterly.

"But who is controlling time? How could my memory work without time?"

"You will battle those thoughts when the TIME comes. That sentence is no longer so simple is it?" Artems shook her head no.

"Well, what of my world? How can I find it? I want to feel it and not just see it!"

"Everything not forbidden is compulsory, my dear. So you've already seen your world. All of space exists on timelines. This is a question of merging lines, merging your present copy of reality without your parents with a copy in which you and your parents are together." Artemis listened fearlessly. "So there is a timeline where you've already discovered how to merge copies. To enter that world, merely align with the memory of who already entered and found it." Artemis bowed her head and tried to recall the memory of already finding her parents. Nothing came.

"Why can't I remember that!" Artemis cried.

"Do not fret my dear. Use something beyond words and thoughts to tap into that memory. Try another frequency besides the thought frequency. Tune to your Star Heart."

"But what happens at the intersections? What happens when I enter that world? I'm so frightened!"

"Only you and courage will ever know the answer to that. It takes courage and love to see me Artemis. Look closer. Look at what lies behind my eyes." Artemis looked deeply into Kala's blue infinities and noticed on the sheet music the same pattern of symbols that was on the construction sign in the Emerald Forest. "You are not seeing me because of thought. Your great heart is what is seeing me."

Artemis realized this was also how she saw the 111 on Valentinas' chest. Tears streamed down Artemis' fur. She did not know what to make of this.

Kala spoke on. "Your friends are made of illuminated love. Have you not noticed?" Artems looked at her friends. "They are your reflections and your innermost dreams. They have been the whole time. I will freeze the gap. Have a look. They are illusions."

Artemis ran up to Valentinas and stretched out her paw. It passed right through him! She ran to Jimfinity. Her paw passed right through his pink fur. Artemis gasped. They were each glowing holograms. Kala continued.

"They are your mirrors, Artemis." Kala unfroze the gap.

"We believe in you Artemis!" Exclaimed everyone. This revelation was so completely overwhelming! Artemis dried her tears, clutched her purple locket, and glowed with joy.

"I need everyone's help!"

"Certainly!"

An infinite set of glass doors appeared and Kala smiled. "Time IS a solarium." Artems knew exactly what to do. After all, this was her most dear thought.

"If time is a solarium, then each glass door is a future-memory. So let us find the memory of my family!"

"Splendid! Which door shall we try? There are infinitely many doors!" Valentinas exclaimed.

"This door looks delightful!" Jim pointed to the door etched in the marking $10^{10^{28}}$.

"I don't know what $10^{10^{28}}$ means, but sure I'll try this one!" Artems smiled.

She opened door $10^{10^{28}}$. Inside was a Polychromaticism Garden with a note written by light ray semitones "The colors are for you— Love, Rosenthall." Artemis wondered if this was the home of the Color people at the Multiversity? Was it so special it needed its own place? For, while similar to the Multiversity, it felt different. Artems recalled Multicorn saying there was enough Hilbert Space for all, so perhaps this was the Hilbert Space of that Hilbert Space, all in inception? Since this world was inside one door belonging to the realm of infinity future-memory glass doors, it was clearly very special.

"Rosenthall???" Jimfinity glowed. "I always knew you were a miracle frequency, Rosey! With your emeralds and goldens, you've made yourself into a polychromatic wonder garden!" Jim wept in golden joy. "You were never one for totalizing, only flying." Jim smiled a thousand suns with a gaze beyond time. Artemis and Valentinas smiled as they'd never seen Jim so happy. He was speaking from the land of suns and they did not question him but hugged him dearly.

Artems had heard of polychromatic music and could not wait to see how a garden could grow in those sort of scales! They ran inside and saw fields of light-rays harnessing rainbows. "Wow! It's a light ray multi-garden, Jim!" Artems exclaimed. Jimfinity could not believe these polymath-creatures could manipulate rainbows, for rainbows were emergent and made of pure geometry. The sky was a delta-function distribution of color, displaying sudden shifts between red and blue, and sparkling foods grew straight from the rainbows. A dynamical honey dew, with a light ray root system, changing color from the deepest mint green to the lightest OZ green, dangled out of the sky and appeared right by Artem's face. She graciously took it and shared it with everyone. "Thank you! It's so delicious!" Artemis pondered all of the wonderful sounds coming from the rainbows. They sounded imaginary and like pure color. The honey dew sounded OZ green. The sky sounded blue. This whole world was a synesthete sonic architecturality.

The land adjacent to the light ray fields was made of books, jurassic color palettes, and walkable music scales based on a two-dimensional semitone system: one dimension was light rays and the other imaginary numbers.

"It's a multi-dimensional semitone system, since each dimension is already an infinity." Jimfinity gasped. Upon encountering any gaps in the land, one could pull a rainbow from the sky, bend it into a bridge to cross the gap, and return the rainbow to the sky. Artemis saw huge avocado trees growing out of the book part of the land, airplanes growing from the color palette part of the land, and winged horses with lion faces and bodies made of multiple harps growing from the xenharmonic music scales.

"The light rays grow on music scales, but the music scales are made of light rays!" Artems smiled.

"And all of the creatures have harp bodies! Are their genomes also based on the semitones?" Jimfinity exclaimed. "It's profound. Imagine our double-stranded DNA system being an actual two dimensional system with one strand composed of light rays and the other the imaginary number system." Artemis and Valentinas twirled in excitement.

Harp-children and harp-animals conducted the sky into sunrises and sunsets. Butterflies tuned oceans like water harps since these creatures had immediate access to weather and sonorities. Rose bushes scaled molecular reassembly. Aquatic creatures learned quantum numbers and memory retrodiction. Snow dragons watered fields where the twenty fundamental constants grew. When, occasionally, inertial masses inverted, causing the sky and land to also invert, the poly-creatures knew the snow dragons were having fun. Artems smiled as she had seen similar ideas at the Multiversity lectures. Upon closer inspection, Artems noticed that all of the poly-creatures wore tweed jackets and purple lockets, had bodies made of harps, and possessed colored, mutable, omni dimensional eyes like Valentinas.

Hearing a burst of cheers and praise, Artems peered further into the doorway and saw a team of blue pups praising a red haired pink harp-lioness for sustaining entropy reversal for three zeptoseconds. "A pink lioness reversed entropy! She must be changing the ratio of manifestation of space to time. And if she can do that, she can surely change Planck's constant of action!" Jimfinity exclaimed. "I must meet her Artems! Action is mathematical and she understands it!" Valentinas agreed.

"A fine idea! The garden is such a lovely place and everyone looks so precocious and kind. Let's do say hello." Jimfinity ran to the pink harp-lioness and commented on her stunning tweed jacket and she had pardonably no notice of him. He was taken back by her eyes. Her eyes were solid bubblegum pink, containing no pupil, and displayed different intensities of the bubblegum pink color. Jimfinity exclaimed.

"I wanted to congratulate you on your expertise! I, without excellence, have been attempting the same for years!" The pink harp-lioness pulled out a packet of pencils and carried on talking with the pups. The pups took no notice of Jimfinity.

"Her eyes . . . It seems they cannot see us? I wish they could!" Valentinas exclaimed.

"I wonder if they cannot see us because they are so used to seeing in the light ray semitones?" Jim replied. Artems reflected in series.

"Multicorn said adepts were not identified with conventional seeing. And the Color People are clearly adepts reinventing sonority. And they can only hear what time is. And time is only what they can see and their eyes see semitones. So, they DO see us! It's just in infinite semitones!" Artemis jumped in joy at her discovery and Valentinas and Jim jumped with her. "Remember how the Color People in the Multiversity looked at us as if they knew? As if they were seeing us beyond simple sight."

They came across a silver dais where a blue Harp-Centaur was feasting on light rays. They could not understand the level of photosynthetic mastery to do this. Artems wondered what would happen if the Harp-Centaur ate all of the light rays leaving the semitone system based only on the imaginary dimension. Jimfinity approached the Harp-Centaur.

"My dear sir, may I ask how you've come about to eat light rays?

We do well to eat organic where I come from. Also what a fine jacket you're wearing and that purple collar is splendid!" To his surprise, the Harp-Centaur noticed him and spoke, but spoke in arcane equalities.

"ER = EPR," said the Harp-Centaur calmly, and proceeded to eat the light rays. Jimfinity was taken back, as this was one of the most powerful physics equations of post-general relativity. The blue Centaur had peculiar eyes as well. They were solid white, displaying in indigo blue the equations of what he was presently thinking.

"What does he mean?" inquired Artemis. "And why can he see us?" She thought to herself, "Is it because he eats the light rays?"

"I can explain it all to you soon, Artemis. But I need to clarify a few things. Are you saying that is how you eat the light rays? Using wormholes?" Jimfinity exclaimed.

"SO(32) E(8)," exclaimed the Centaur-wizard. Artemis looked amazed but was confused. A Diapsalmata of glass walked by debating the sociological isomorphisms inherent in circle languages.

"Indeed. By mastering retrodiction, their language is free to be non-linear," Jimfinity commented to himself, while everyone else was amazed at the intellectual and physical fitness of the walking Diapsalmata.

The Harp-Centaur nodded in excellence to the passing glass and returned his attention to Artemis, her friends, and his lunch of rays. Jimfinity deciphered the Centaur's last equality and gasped.

"Artems, this is not the world with your parents in it. But we are close." The Harp-Centaur turned to Jimfinity, bowed, and ascended into the sky, leaving the remaining light rays on the dais. Artemis cheered in joy.

"I always wanted to eat light rays!" Everyone ran up to the light rays and suddenly found themselves in front of the door $10^{10^{28}}$, where they earlier began.

"What happened?" Artems inquired.

"It absolutely disappeared!" Valentinas cried.

"First the Multiversity disappears! And now the entire Polychromatic Garden?" Jimfinity pondered.

"But it disappeared where?" Artemis pondered.

Adjacent to the $10^{10^{28}}$ door was another glass door engraved in $10^{10^{29}}$. Emboldened by joy and the strength of her friends, and maybe in shock from seeing the poly garden both bloom and vanish, Artemis opened the door and to her surprise saw an identical copy of she and her friends entering the room from the other side wearing the same clothes, having the same demeanor, and containing the same arrangement of quarks. It is as if the room was a hologram duplicate of the *real* Artemis, Jimfinity, and Valentinas. What would happen if they approached the copy?

All of the creatures tried to approach their doubles. But their doubles ran from them.

"Oh, this will never work!" Jimfinity exclaimed. "They are our exact copy. They have the same thoughts. They will never turn toward us since they are trying to find us as well!"

"Wait, they are only our copy because they have the same exact memories. If we could figure out how to keep all memories the same up until this point and only change THIS one, we could enter their room," Artemis exclaimed, proud of herself for making such a connection.

"Brilliant! But how!" Jimfinity asked. "For that would win you all the Nobel Multi Prizes Artems!" Artemis began.

"Kala, I need your help! We need to create a gap within the gap!" All of her friends looked bewildered as Kala recounted "remember your star." Artemis continued. "Let me explain. Kala, since you have mastered being in multiple places at once, can you simultaneously be here with us and do something different in $10^{10^{29}}$ right NOW. That will make one different memory strand and then we can enter the room!" Everyone cheered in joy and Kala smiled.

"Of course! Now you're flying thinking! Remember when you were a pilot?"

"Why I do not recall such a thing?" That was enough! A different memory strand was created. Kala created the gap within the gap. Artemis and her friends quickly ran past the $10^{10^{29}}$ door and all six creatures, the originals plus the copies ran towards each other.

The Artems twins, speaking at the same time, exclaimed.

"How could this be!"

"How could this be!"

"You're me!"

"You're me!"

"Tell me something only I would know!"

"Tell me something only I would know!"

"Tell me about Sasha and Valentinas!"

"Tell me about Sasha and Valentinas!"

"Oh, my goodness great heavens!"

"Oh, my goodness great heavens!" After a long pause, the fear began to fade.

"What were you thinking about just now?"

"What were you thinking about just now?"

"Coconuts!"

"Coconuts!"

"Oh, mercy."

"Oh, mercy." A long pause commenced. Jimfinity had his own conversation with *himself*.

"That Harris tweed looks phenomenal"

"That Harris tweed looks phenomenal"

"Thank you. Everyone knows only real time-loop bunnies wear tweed."

"Thank you. Everyone knows only real time-loop bunnies wear tweed."

"But I'm the real Jimfinity"

"But I'm the real Jimfinity."

"Time is an inaccessible cardinal."

"Time is an inaccessible cardinal."

"The subterfuge! I'm convinced!"

"The subterfuge! I'm convinced!" They gasped and stared at each other amazed. The double Valentinas spoke.

"Your wondrous infinity Antlers!"

"Your wondrous infinity Antlers!"

"Have you seen little Golden?"

"Have you seen little Golden?"

"Did you see what I did to recreate the Snow Land?"

"Did you see what I did to recreate the Snow Land?" After the double creatures spoke their double talk, everyone was completely confused as to who was the original copy of the double set. The Artemis twins spoke.

"Don't you see the glass is a time-loop?"

"Don't you see the glass is a time-loop?"

"The solarium is a time-loop!"

"The solarium is a time-loop!" All the creatures gasp!

"But how can this be? We are so far away from normal time."

"But how can this be? We are so far away from normal time."

"How can you have my same memories? And only in THIS door?"

"How can you have my same memories? And only in THIS door?"

Both Kalas answer.

"Think Artemis. Think!"

"Think Artemis. Think!" The Artemis twins reply.

"Oh! That's what the $10^{10^{29}}$ means! It is a distance. Ten to the ten to the twenty-ninth power away from us!"

"Oh! That's what the $10^{10^{29}}$ means! It is a distance. Ten to the ten to the twenty-ninth power away from us!"

"How curious! If I leave, then you'll leave? Will you still remain you? Or do we swap bodies and memories? What a grand mirror world!"

"How curious! If I leave, then you'll leave? Will you still remain you? Or do we swap bodies and memories? What a grand mirror world!"

All the creatures stared at their mirror doubles and bowed. The Artemis twins spoke.

"But look, Jimfinity. We cannot touch. How can my thoughts transfer, but my physical form cannot? What is this barrier?"

"But look, Jimfinity. We cannot touch. How can my thoughts transfer, but my physical form cannot? What is this barrier?" Both Jims replied.

"Don't forget, Artems! The only way you are able to approach this identical copy is because you are in the time gap. The barrier must be the intersection between normal time and the time gap!"

"Don't forget, Artems! The only way you are able to approach this identical copy is because you are in the time gap. The barrier must be the intersection between normal time and the time gap!" Both Artemises look at him aghast!

"But what of ordinal time? What of looking-glass time? Yesterday has always been my looking glass."

"But what of ordinal time? What of looking-glass time? Yesterday has always been my looking glass."

The Jims continue.

"Be careful Artmis! Who knows what would happen if we broke the barrier!"

"Be careful Artmis! Who knows what would happen if we broke the barrier!"

Everyone gasped!

WHITE ON WHITE ON WHITE ON WHITE ON WHITE O NW HITE ONW HITE O N W H I T E.

CHAPTER 7

GLASSED UNICORNS OF UNITARITY

"ARTEMS? ARTEMS?" THE SOUNDS WERE CRYSTAL water pouring over her ears. The words rained inside her mind and enchanted into indescribable letters.

"Aretmis! Artemis! Please wake up!" Jimfinity screamed.

"What happened?" Artemis awoke with her eyes heavy as a thousand stars.

"You fainted my dear. It seemed as if you left us in the mind . . ."

"Are we still with our doubles?"

"No. Only one set remains," Valentinas smiled.

"Are we the real ones?" Artems inquired. Jimfinity grinned.

"Let us hope so, for we will never know. Your quantum twin would have all the same memories as you remember?"

"I feel so funny. Like I have thousands of new memories."

"What do you mean new memories?" Valentinas inquired.

"I can access them all at once. Where's Kala?"

All of a sudden an illuminated door with the golden numbers $10^{10^{35}}$ appeared. Artemis yelped. "Curiouser times infinity! Ten to the ten to the thirty-fifth . . . it's the dimension of . . . of . . . why can't I remember?" The door $10^{10^{35}}$ was as tall as the length of the gaze upon it and housed an incredible padlock of elliptic curves. "However shall we open this?" Artemis tried all the possible combinations of arcane mathematics patterns she knew, all to no avail. She wept and her friends encouraged her.

"Try your Star Heart. You can do it, Artemis. We believe in you!!"

Artems's eyes turned emerald and begin to glow as did her purple locket.

"I'm ready, Jim." Artems sang a Gold Nightingale song from her childhood and with Pegasus strength entered 111 on the keypad. The door opened onto a quaint rose garden. She recognized it immediately! It was the garden to her home. Her emerald eyes streamed emerald infinities of tears, blanketing her white fur.

"Jimfinity! It's home!"

She ran so quickly to her home that not even a light-speed-Cauchy Cheetah could out-run her! Jimfinity was right behind her, hoping as fast as he could, and her purple locket glowed infinitely. She burst through the door and thamaturgically changed back into Shanna form, her red hair glowing. Jimfinity changed back into a stuffed bunny. Her parents were inside and Sasha, her beautiful lilac point Siamese, jumped in her arms! Shanna cried infinite tears and her parents could not believe their eyes! The room was lit with the light between double rainbows.

"Mom! Dad! Oh, my goodness! You're here! You're not just a memory. You're really here!" Her parents wept and held her with the arms of eternity. Sasha ran up to Shanna. "Sasha! Oh, baby girl! You're well! You can walk again!" Her mother spoke.

"Go ahead, Sasha. Show Panna how you can walk." Sasha meowed so grandly and licked Shanna. She jumped down and walked the entire living room. She walked like a King.

"Oh, Sasha!! How wonderful!" Tears streamed down her face and Shanna's heart bloomed a thousand suns. She was filled with such imaginable joy. Sasha ran and jumped back into Shanna's arms and Sasha's purple eyes and Shanna's emerald eyes locked in a love that was eternal and infinite. Nothing could ever transcend that highest ordinal of affection. Her whole family and Sasha had a halo glow about them. This whole world did.

"I awoke in that terrible hospital! I wasn't even there to tell you goodbye."

"Rest dear. It was out of your hands. How are your dreams? Have you built your infinity clock yet out of your favorite pencils?"

"Oh, mother! I'm trying. I really am. I hope I don't one day run out of pencils. And did you know today I imagined time was a solarium?" Her parents smiled.

"I bet you did! Here. An endless supply of pencils just for you". Shanna's mother smiled and handed her a small satchel containing eleven sparkly pink pencils. Shanna glowed and twirled around with the satchel, modeling it for Sasha's approval. But then Shanna recalled where she was and was deeply saddened.

"But where have you all been? I've been so alone, although the Multicorn and the Multiversity seem to be my second home!"

"The Multiversity? And a multicorn? Oh, Shanna, what marvelous adventures you have been on!"

"Yes, they are pure wonder, but I miss you. I don't want everything to be a future memory." Shanna wept and kissed Sasha on her purple forehead.

"Don't cry, baby girl. We will always be here with you. Now you know how to always find us."

"If I ever want to visit you all again, I just have to use my Star

Heart." They all smile and Sasha danced and circled around in her arms. Shanna had found her home in time; it was in the Star-Heart-charts of multi-time.

"Oh, I've missed you all so much. Now we can all be together again." Suddenly, flying overhead at incredible speed, came a blast of eleven jeweled unicorns. They were the Unicorns of Unitarity. They were the vertices of the time crystal.

"Move along! Move along!" They cried in their lavish Andromeda XXII voices. Shanna looked up, confused.

"Unicorns?"

"This is a close out! All dimensions must go!" They shouted. Whatever space they flew by, they alchemized it to normal time by dropping clocks everywhere! These were no ordinary clocks. They had multiple faces with etched-in symbols of ordinals that were the very opposite of static numbers. Shanna was so confused as to what was being measured, since the very symbols themselves were dynamical. As if the confusion wasn't bad enough, the sound was unbearable! It was the simultaneous sound of time fusion and time fission. The unicorns were forcing multi-dream time into linear time, much to the resistance of multi-time. Shanna's parents and Sasha started to fade away.

"Wait! Please! Was it something I said? Let me stay!" Her parents looked at her with calm eyes. Eyes forever Narnian. They did not see the unicorns. It was as if they were behind so many sets of glass. Glass that was not elemental. Glass that was out of reach of the clocks and unicorns.

Out of reach of any *thing*. Out of reach.

"The glass! You're glassing! Please come back!" But they could not hear the glass and they could not hear for the glass.

Sasha meowed over and over again and smiled her purple marble eyes, raising her purple paws. Her parents spoke one last time.

"We love you Shanna! We love you so much, baby girl!!"

Shanna cried. "Wait! Please don't go! You're becoming the

solarium!" But their eyes could hear her no longer. "Wait, this is not right! They are unicorns! Have they forgotten what they are? Whose memory are they?" In the cacophony of clocks, Shanna hugged her parents and Sasha deeply. But they were only outlines—what exists before the image. Alone in supplication, Shanna pleaded for their full selves to return! But the problem in this space was with the *re-*. How can anything *re*-turn in a time gap? No form remained. Only voices and Sasha's little purple meow, red shifted to infinity.

"Remember us. Remember us. With. That. Incomparable. Love."

Non-chromatic sounds like supernovas of mighty ships and Arch Angel cries of great winged horses filled the room as dimensions were collapsing and linear time was being birthed again. Oh, the sounds of dimensional birth! How could one remember being alive at a genesis?

Jimfinity, still stuffed, spoke. "Artems, they are the unicorns of unitarity! They are breaking the barrier and returning us to normal space. Say goodbye."

"But I thought nothing ends, Jimmy? How could normal time return when we are in the gap?"

Jimfinity's eyes obtained. And obtained for Shanna's entire life. "Oh, goodbye. Goodbye, Sasha. I love you. I love you. I love you!"

CHAPTER 8

LUX IMMORTALEM TAUTOLOGY

SHANNA AWOKE IN THE HOSPITAL ROOM. NATASHA, THE orderly with Aslan golden hair, was making her bed, highly aware of Shanna's curious state.

"Hi, Shanna."

Shanna heard her, but it was below perception, at the frequency of the deep organs. Shanna was crying stars, but in this reality they were merely tears. Her red hair was wet from the star crying and her purple locket glistened. Natasha knew how to comfort Shanna and to alchemize her star-tears into their true joy.

"You're a little flushed honey. It's quite nice to see you rather pink! Why I think this calls for a celebration!" She changed Shanna's white sheet to a pink sheet. Shanna laughed and her star-tears dried into lovely pink crystal salts.

"A new pink sheet for you! Now, to what wonderful places have you been today?"

"Oh, Natasha, I've been to so many places. I was greeted by a Multicorn at the Multiversity who showed me the future of mathematics and physics. The so so difficult but so so exciting futurist future." Natasha smiled.

"I don't understand those things too well, but I love hearing your imaginings. Please, go on."

Shanna was sustained in her dream state and remembered the inner thoughts and future happenings of Valentinas and even little Golden. Sasha's purple eyes. How could she access the others so easily? Was she truly an adept of multi-awareness now? She tried to explain to Natasha.

"When I remember my star, it is as if I have access to the memories and timelines of everyone. It's so curious."

"Wow, that sounds so amazing to have a star that you can remember. It's so special to be able to access that much. Please, tell me what it is like?"

"What what is like?"

"To access that general memory bank?"

"It feels like my mind is OZ. Natasha, I saw my family in this beautiful illuminated world." Natasha glowed.

"Oh, Shanna! I'm so happy for you! What world? What did they say? You finally found them!"

"I love them so much. I miss them so much! May I have my pencil pack and some paper? I will show you!"

"Of course!"

Shanna excitedly picked up her pencils and began working on calculations to scale the neutrino-based CPT violation to look for the mirror galaxy, which she believed might be a wormhole to the Level 2 Multiverse, which housed her family and Sasha. But such a funny thing happened with the integrals. They all diverged.

"Curious," Shanna thought. She tried a simpler calculation. It diverged as well.

Natasha inquired. "Is everything okay?"

Shanna continued. She tried the most simple calculation $1 + 0$ and found the result even more perplexing.

"$1 + 0 = 0$? Have I left the Euclidean world so that I am in some sort of abelian ring?" Then it dawned on her! "There must be a glitch in the Level 4 Multiverse, which, since it is a part of all of the other levels, will affect them all! Mathematical existence equals physical existence. Oh, dear! If the math is off, then the physics will be too!" Shanna paused. "Wait. Is the time gap the Level 4 Multiverse? The home of my family?" Shanna smiled. "Why, that's it!!"

Shanna looked at the sky, but it was nowhere to be found. Nor was Natasha. Cardinality was not of this place and a solarium knows no absence. The equations were erasing themselves, in a reverse entropic fashion. "How is entropy reversing but I am still the same? My blood isn't flowing the other direction I don't think!" She laughed nervously, hoping her thoughts would not immediately create such an unpleasant phenomena as sudden circulation reversal!

In the absent-sky, the eleven Unicorns of Unitarity appeared and spoke. "Dear Shanna Blu, there has been a rupture in the Level 4 Multiverse. We ask you to summon your Level 1 Galactic Council of Wizards and travel to Level 4 to fix the error. Yes, you will have to turn yourself into a mathematical shape. Good Luck!"

Shanna's mind began to churn excitedly, planning her change to a mathematical shape. "First, I shall fix the appropriate gauge allowing for negative dimensional moduli spaces, which must have negative curvature. Then I can be in ADS space. I can use ADS/CFT duality to turn myself into a conformal field, using the Energy Time Uncertainty Principle, cue the spectral covers to build my Hodge-Tate spectral sequence, since only my cohomology is necessary, and degenerate the sequence at E1. Oh, what is the relation between cohomology and conformal fields? Should I make the conformal field an algebraic group tensored with a spectral sequence? Then I will take the E1 degeneration as a highly non-geometric Gepner point, and compressed in this point is all of my information, which contains all of the stars from the cosmic origin. It is like a Drinfeld tower, an infinity stack, and more properly, an $(\infty, 1)$ stack, since we need all of the arrows reversible so I can get back home! Once I again land in ADS, I can invert the topological suspension to get back to positive curvature. This will require some Vieta jumping, but I can do it. I can save Level 4 to save my world." Shanna applauded herself and jumped out of the bed as if she was Coleman Dobson delivering her double keynotes.

"Good day everyone! Today I shall turn myself into an infinity stack and all without methodological solipsism."

And you can find the next adventure of Artemis Blu without methodological solipsism in the next series. But, since this was all written non locally, you already read it and yesterday is your looking glass. For this would all obtain with or without you reading it, given memory is an Illumination Cantor Set and Shanna made a multi-time loop with herself. This very book could be your double awareness, since it was hers.

From the Solarium of Artemis Blu, we say to you,

Remember, retrodictively, your star.

ᚦᚻᛖ ᚱᛖ-ᛖᚾᛞ

THE RE-END

ABOUT THE AUTHOR

Shanna is a mathematician, researcher, and author studying Derived Mirror Symmetry and Grand Unified Theories of Mathematics and Physics. She also intersects Lie Algebras with Continental Thought in Perfectoid-Wittengstein moduli.

.

ACKNOWLEDGMENTS

I would like to thank Guy, Jule, and Karen for finding a home in time for this dream of mine. I would also like to thank my friends and my family for your uncountably infinite support and electric discussions of this life wonderland. My sweet Keats brother for your angelic love and phoenix heart. My DaVinci Polymath for your eternity. My mother for your OZ. My love for you all, Shanna.

57703428R00062

Made in the USA
Columbia, SC
13 May 2019